GM0036000I0

Hamlyn nature guides

Mushrooms & Toadstools

Hamlyn nature guides

Mushrooms & Toadstools

Ronald Rayner

Hamlyn
London · New York · Sydney · Toronto

Foreword

The aim of this nature guide is to provide a book that may be easily consulted in the field and by which the more common of the larger fungi (mushrooms, toadstools and their allies) may be identified. In all there are around 3500 species of the larger fungi to be found in Europe but the majority of these are infrequently met with. The 220 species illustrated in this publication have been carefully chosen so as to be sufficient for the identification of a high proportion of those likely to be encountered. The selection was based on a statistical survey, recently carried out by the writer, of the frequency with which species have been recorded over a period of eighteen years on excursions organized by the British Mycological Society to 253 localities. The results of this survey are regarded as being representative for Europe as a whole. All the species that were frequent enough to be found in 5 per cent or more of the localities are described in this book and some additional edible and poisonous species have been included, as well as a few which have greater frequency of occurrence in mainland Europe.

Measurements In the descriptions of the species, measurements are given in the metric system and abbreviated: cm=centimetres, mm=millimetres. For the stems of fungi, the first figure given refers to the length and the second to the width.

Front jacket: Hypholoma fasciculare
back jacket: Oudimansiella mucida
title spread: Pholiota adiposa

Line drawings by Laura Mason

Published by The Hamlyn Publishing Group Limited
London · New York · Sydney · Toronto
Astronaut House, Feltham, Middlesex, England
Copyright © The Hamlyn Publishing Group Limited 1979

ISBN 0 600 36283 3

All rights reserved. No part of this publication may be reproduced, stored in a retrieval system, or transmitted, in any form or by any means, electronic, mechanical, photocopying, recording or otherwise, without the permission of The Hamlyn Publishing Group Limited.

Phototypeset by Photocomp Ltd, Birmingham, England
Printed in Italy

Contents

Introduction

Fungi are a large and important class of organisms with a wide range of forms. They are peculiar in having a mode of nutrition similar to that of animals, whilst their structure is more akin to that of plants. Thus, they are dependent for their sustenance, and so for their source of energy for growth, on complex carbon compounds manufactured by other organisms. These they obtain by growing on the living or dead bodies of these organisms. In contrast, the great majority of plants absorb energy from the sun's radiation and employ this to build up complex carbon compounds from carbon dioxide in the air, water and minerals. Fungi consist in the main of thin, usually branching, filaments called *hyphae* made up of tubular cells placed end to end. These hyphae grow through the material from which nutrients are being obtained, such as soil, wood or other plant material or occasionally living or dead animals. They form a very fine, tenuous, loose and cobweb-like weft called the *mycelium*, which is normally barely visible to the naked eye except when grouped into cords. The mycelium is the body of the fungus and is roughly equivalent to the roots, stem and leaves of a flowering plant, but is ordinarily hidden from view in the soil or other medium in which the fungus is growing.

What are commonly referred to as mushrooms or toadstools are, in fact, the reproductive bodies and are the only parts that can normally be seen. They are equivalent to the flowers and fruit of a flowering plant and they produce the spores by which the fungus is disseminated. The spores may be likened to seeds but do not contain an embryonic plant and, usually consist instead, of a single cell. They are also much smaller, being invisible to the naked eye since they range in size, according to species, from 0·001 to 0·025 millimetres (1 to 25 microns) long. These spores are often produced in very large numbers, a single fruit-body of the Common Mushroom producing 16 000 million, and are usually liberated into the air to be carried away by air currents. On landing on a suitable spot, the spore germinates and a hypha grows out and branches to form a mass of mycelium.

Many fungi have fruit-bodies that are minute and their structure can only be made out by using a lens or a microscope. They are often referred to as *microfungi* and they include the yeasts, moulds, mildews, rusts, smuts, and so on. The larger or *macrofungi* are those whose fruit-bodies can easily be seen by the naked eye and it is only with these that the present book is concerned.

Fungus names

As with all organisms, fungi have been given double-barrelled scientific names of Latin or Greek derivation. The second of these names denotes the kind or species and the first the genus or clan. Species are grouped together into a genus because they have certain resemblances to each other and may have one or more characteristics in common. The names may seem cumbersome and strange to people not used to them, but have the advantage of showing the relationship between species, as well as being standardized and widely used. Further, with the majority of fungi, no true English name exists although many have been invented. For those who may prefer to use them, English names, including a selection of 'invented' ones, will be given. Even scientific names may be changed from time to time as the result of research, so whilst the most up-to-date have been used in this book, in the descriptions of species, they are followed by the more commonly encountered older ones in brackets.

Edibility

Doubtless many users of this book will be interested primarily in the gastronomic aspects of fungus hunting and in being able to recognize which fungi are good to eat and which are worthless or even poisonous. This has been kept in mind in selecting the species to be illustrated.

It cannot be too strongly stressed that there are no simple tests by which the edible may be distinguished from the poisonous species. People must learn to recognize each species separately by its distinctive characteristics. Very young specimens in the 'button' stage should be avoided as those of poisonous species may easily be confused with those of edible species, as the distinctive characters may not have been developed. It is also wise, when trying a new species for the first time, to eat only one or two fruit-bodies, since the effects of a misidentification may thus be minimized and personal idiosyncrasies tested. Some people are made ill by species that are eaten with impunity by others.

Although relatively few fungi are poisonous, some 2 to 3 per cent of the total number, of these some are deadly even if only a part of a single fruit-body is eaten, so *do not eat any unfamiliar species unless certain that ALL its characteristics are the same as those described for it.*

In the descriptions that accompany the illustrations, one asterisk (*) following the name of the species denotes that it is moderately good to eat and two that it is very good. A dagger (†) indicates that it is moderately poisonous and two that it is very poisonous. When no symbol is given, either the fungus has little or no culinary value, or no information is available.

Structure of the fruit-body

The larger fungi are divided into two main groups, the spore-shooters or **Ascomycetes** and the spore-droppers or **Basidiomycetes** or more correctly, the Ascomycotina and Basidiomycotina. In the former the spores are produced, usually eight at a time, inside microscopic, normally rather elongated, club-shaped sacks called *asci*. Most frequently they are liberated by pressure building up inside the ascus which ruptures at the tip, and the spores are shot out violently several millimetres into the air. Many Ascomycetes have very small fruit-bodies and so are outside the scope of this book.

The larger Ascomycetes belong to three groups. In the **Discomycetes**, which include the disc or cup fungi and the morels, the asci are closely packed alongside each other to form a smooth lining to the upper surface of a disc or cup, an erect club, or a variously convoluted or honey-combed head, carried aloft on a distinct stem.

In the **Pyrenomycetes** or flask fungi, the asci line the inside of tiny flask-shaped cavities called *perithecia*, set into the surface of the fruit-body. The asci are orientated so that their spores are shot out through the mouth of the cavity.

Fig. 1 A Discomycete:
Bladder Elf-cup
(*Peziza vesiculosa*)

Longitudinal section of fruit-body

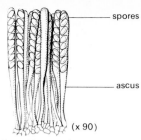

spores

ascus

(x 90)

Part of inner surface

The perithecia may be seen with a lens if a fruit-body is cut across, and their mouths may be seen on the surface as minute pimples. The flesh of the fruit-bodies may be soft and variously coloured or may be hard, black and charcoal-like. The fruit-body shapes range from a flat crust, through rounded cushion-shapes to erect clubs or antler-like growths.

In the truffle fungi or **Tuberales** the asci are formed in a mass of tissue inside a more or less globose fruit-body which is buried in the soil. The spores are dispersed by animals eating, or tunnelling into, the fruit-bodies.

In some Ascomycetes spores of another type called *conidia* are produced. These may form a powder over the surface as in the Candle-snuff Fungus, *Xylaria hypoxylon* (page 18) or a moist layer dispersed by rain as in *Ascocoryne sarcoides* (page 16).

Although the distinguishing characteristic of the Ascomycetes, the ascus, can only be seen with a microscope, that a fungus belongs to this group may also be deduced by placing a fruit-body, or the head alone if it has a distinct stalk, in its natural position on a sheet of paper or preferably glass, and placing a cover such as a glass jar over it. After a few hours a white or coloured spore deposit will form as a broad halo around the fruit-body since the spores are shot out for a considerable distance from it. If a Basidiomycete fruit-body is treated similarly, a spore deposit will form only immediately underneath it and there is no broad halo. In these fungi the spores are produced on small prongs, usually four in number, that form on the tops of short, microscopic, club-shaped cells called *basidia*. The spores are often shot off these but only for a very short

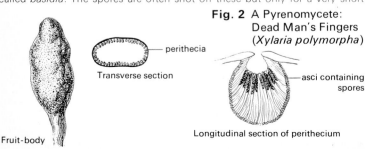

Fig. 2 A Pyrenomycete:
Dead Man's Fingers
(*Xylaria polymorpha*)

perithecia

Transverse section

Fruit-body

asci containing
spores

Longitudinal section of perithecium

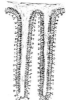
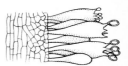

Fig. 3 A Basidiomycete:
Field Mushroom
(*Agaricus campestris*)

Fruit-body with vertical slice
cut from cap margin

Gills cut across
their length

Basidia with spores

distance, and then begin to fall and are carried away by air currents. In still air they fall vertically so that they are then deposited immediately below the surface on which they were produced. When the cap of a gill-fungus is placed gills downwards, the spore deposit mirrors the pattern of the gills.

In the Basidiomycetes a considerable range of fruit-body shapes is found. The simplest is a flat crust that grows on the sides or lower surfaces of branches, logs and so on. In some species, the upper margin of such a crust may grow outwards to form a shelf or bracket. In others a simple flap without a crust is produced. In the fairy club fungi (*Clavariaceae*), the fruit-bodies form erect clubs or branched structures like tiny trees. These shapes are also found in the Ascomycete genera *Xylaria* (page 18), *Geoglossum* (page 16) and *Cordyceps* (page 18), as well as in *Calocera* (page 20) amongst the jelly fungi.

In many Basidiomycetes there is a well-developed horizontal portion or cap supported on a stem that is usually central but may be attached towards or at one side. The spore-bearing surface may be smooth, have tubercles or spines, be variously wrinkled or consist of tubes or radiating vertical plates called gills, as in the Field Mushroom. The gill-fungi or agarics are the largest and most important group of the Basidiomycetes.

The jelly fungi are a small group distinguished by the jelly-like nature of their flesh. In shape they may consist of irregular masses of jelly, downwardly directed discs or cups, brackets or even horn or antler-like erect growths as in *Calocera* (page 20). Gelatinous fruit-bodies are also found in the Ascomycete genera *Ascocoryne* (page 16) and *Bulgaria* (page 14).

The Gasteromycetales or stomach fungi are another distinct group of Basidiomycetes and in these the spores are produced in masses *inside* the fruit-body. At maturity the mass may become powdery and be vented to the atmosphere through an orifice in the top of the fruit-body or the whole fruit-body wall may break up. In the stink-horns the spore mass is finally carried up into the air on a stalk. The spores are embedded in evil-smelling mucous that attracts flies which eat it, thus dispersing the spores.

Characters used for identification

The shapes that the fruit-body may assume and the forms of the spore-bearing surfaces have been described above and are of prime importance in the identification of fungi. In fungi possessing tubes, the consistency and thickness of the flesh should be noted. In the boletes or sponge-caps it is soft and similar to that of a Field Mushroom and the fungus has a cap with a central stem. If the flesh is tougher, then the fungus is a polypore. It may be merely softly corky and rather dry, or it may be tougher, leathery or even woody. In some species the fruit-body grows for several years, forming a new tube-layer each year.

With gill-fungi it is most important to observe the colour of a thick spore deposit obtained as described earlier. It may be white or very pale coloured, a pinkish cinnamon (often referred to as 'pink'), bright rusty or dull 'cigar'-brown, chocolate, purplish or violet dark brown, grey or black. In the field the spore colour can often be discovered from spore deposits that have accumulated naturally on objects situated below the gills, such as the stem, or ring if present, of the fungus itself, the cap of another fruit-body, leaves and so on. The colour of the gills may also be a guide but must be used with caution: if they are white or pale coloured the spores must also be white, whilst rusty, dark chocolate, violet-brown or black gills usually produce similarly coloured spores. Often a dusting of spore powder, if this is coloured, may be seen on the gills.

The way the gills join the stem is very valuable for distinguishing genera and the terms used are given in the glossary (see fig. 5).

The fruit-bodies of some agarics, when young, are completely surrounded by a thin membrane called a *universal veil*, which is torn apart as the fungus grows. The remnants of the veil at the bottom of the stem may form a sheathing cup called a *volva*, a narrow rim, or a series of woolly scales on the stem base. Similar scales that are flat and moveable may be left on the cap surface. Another membrane, the *partial veil*, may surround the cap only and may, or may not, be accompanied by a universal veil. On expansion of the fruit-body it may leave a

Fig. 4 The fruit-bodies of agarics cut lengthwise to show their veils.

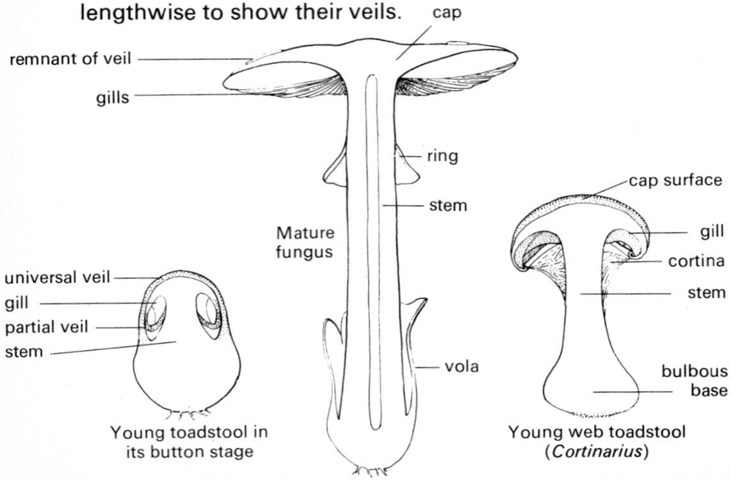

cap

remnant of veil

gills

ring

stem

Mature fungus

cap surface

gill

cortina

stem

universal veil

gill

partial veil

stem

vola

bulbous base

Young toadstool in its button stage

Young web toadstool (*Cortinarius*)

10

membranous or fibrous ring on the stem. Sometimes, in a partially expanded agaric, fibres stretch from the cap margin to the stem forming a tenuous web called a *cortina*.

The type of stem, whether thick or thin, and its flesh are useful characters for distinguishing genera. The flesh may be dense and floccose, breaking easily and cleanly, or it may be fibrous and relatively tough. It is termed *cartilaginous* if when cut across or broken, the exposed surface appears translucent.

Odour may be very useful for distinguishing certain species and may be, for example, reminiscent of meal, bitter almonds, geraniums, apricots, oil, potatoes, crab, fish, bed or plant bugs, garlic and so on. Taste may also be a valuable aid to identification. A small portion, say around a 5 millimetre cube of fungus, especially of the cap and gills, is chewed for a minute or so and then spat out. Provided only such a small amount is tasted, there is no fear of poisoning though known very poisonous species are best avoided. Certain species of *Lactarius* may be identified if a small drop of their milk is tasted.

A careful note should be made of the type of vegetation with which a fungus is growing, especially as regards the species of trees nearby. Many fungus species have very strict requirements in this respect, due to a mutually advantageous relationship between them and the trees.

The application of certain chemicals such as strong ammonia, solutions of caustic alkalis or iodine, or a crystal of iron alum to the surface of a fungus may produce a colour reaction which identifies it. Further information is given in the glossary under the names of the chemicals used.

How to use this book

The simplest way is merely to leaf through the illustrations looking for one that resembles the fungus being identified. Remember that the stomach fungi and stinkhorns are at the end of the book, the fungi without gills at the beginning and the agarics, arranged according to spore colour, occupy the rest of the pages. When an illustration that appears to represent the fungus is found, check carefully through the description to see that the characters given are completely in agreement with those of the specimen.

The illustrations have been arranged roughly according to the main lines of scientific classification since this groups related species together and leads to a better understanding of the characters by which a genus may be recognized and may allow this to be determined even when the species is too uncommon to be illustrated. For those who are interested, this arrangement is as follows:—

Ascomycetes — Spore-shooting fungi.
  Discomycetes: disc and cup fungi, morels and their allies.
  Pyrenomycetes: flask fungi.
Basidiomycetes — Spore-dropping fungi.
  Jelly fungi: Tremellales in the broad sense.
  Aphyllophorales i.e. fungi without gills:
    Fungi with spore-bearing surface smooth to wrinkled or with spines.
    Clavariaceae — fairy clubs:

Polypores: spores produced in tubes or sometimes on gill-like plates; substance tough to woody.

Agaricales: Possessing gills or soft, spongy tubes:

Boletes or sponge caps: spores produced in tubes.

Agarics or gill fungi: subdivided according to spore colour, presence or absence of a veil and character of stem.

Gasteromycetales: stomach fungi.

Key This is of the 'indented' type. Choose which of the alternative descriptions placed underneath each other *at the same distance* from the left-hand page margin (with the same number but different letter) applies to the fungus being identified. The sign ↓ indicates there is another alternative description further down the page. Having chosen the description that applies, repeat the process with the further descriptions under the one chosen and inset slightly to the right. Continue until a description is selected that ends with a generic name or names and/or a page reference. If at any point no description appears to apply, then the fungus may belong to a genus with no common species.

1a   Substance of fungus hard or tough, black and charcoal-like.

    2a   Fungus rounded cushion-shaped   *Daldinia, Hypoxylon* page 18

    2b   Fungus antler-shaped, covered with white powder above, or club-shaped   *Xylaria* page 18

1b   Substance not hard or tough as well as black and charcoal-like.

    3a   Fruit-body globose, at least the inner portion, or pear-shaped, with a mass of brown to black spores inside

        Gasteromycetales (stomach fungi) page 120

    3b   Fruit-body not globose or pear-shaped, no spore mass inside.

        4a   Fruit-body crust-like, growing on the surface of wood, etc.

            5a   Surface more or less smooth

                Peniophora page 24, *Hyphodontia* page 22

            5b   ↓ Surface wrinkled or shallowly ridged   *Phlebia* page 24

            5c   ↓ Surface of very shallow, irregular pores, little more than a network of shallow folds or ridges   *Merulius* page 24

            5d   Surface of pores, the mouths of the tubes 2 millimetres long or more   *Phellinus* page 32

        4b   ↓ Fruit-body a more or less rounded, or convoluted and brain-like, gelatinous mass.

            6a   Yellow or orange   *Dacrymyces, Tremella* page 20

            6b   Lilac   *Ascocoryne* page 16

        4c   ↓ Fruit-body disc, cup or irregularly saucer-shaped with or without a short stem.

            7a   Flesh jelly-like.

                8a   Discs black; surface smooth   *Bulgaria* page 14

                8b   ↓ Discs or cups black; surface minutely pimpled

                    Exidia page 22

                8c   Cups brown, often ridged inside   *Hirneola* page 22

            7b   Flesh not gelatinous

                Aleuria, Peziza, Chlorosplenium page 14

      4d ↓ Fruit-body bracket or flap-shaped, sometimes more or less
            erect   *see sub-section 1 at end of key*
      4e ↓ Fruit-body an erect club, or branched like antlers.
            9a Substance black, hard and tough   *Xylaria* page 18
            9b ↓ Substance gelatinous   *Calocera* page 20
            9c Substance neither black nor gelatinous   fairy clubs page 30
      4f Fruit-body with a head or cap carried on a distinct stem.
            10a ↓ Head without gills or tubes on under surface.
                  11a Evil-smelling with a brown, mucous mass covering head
                        at least when young   *Mutinus, Phallus* page 122
                  11b Not evil smelling, without brown mucous mass
                                          Morchella, Leotia, Helvella page 16
            10b ↓ Cap with spines underneath   *Hydnum* page 30
            10c ↓ Cap with pores, the orifices of tubes, underneath.
                  12a Substance tough and leathery   *Coltricia* page 40
                  12b Substance soft and spongy
                                          Boletus, Suillus, Leccinum page 42
            10d ↓ Cap with longitudinal, anastomosing ridges under-
                  neath   *Cantharellus* page 28
            10e Cap with gills underneath   *see sub-section 2 below.*

Sub-section 1 Bracket or flap fungi
1a Lower surface smooth or wrinkled
      2a Substance gelatinous   *Auricularia* page 22
      2b Substance leathery
            Thelephora, Stereum, Chondrostereum, Hymenochaete pages 26–28
1b ↓ Lower surface with pores at the mouths of tubes   polypores page 32
1c ↓ Lower surface a labyrinth of plates   *Daedalea, Daedaliopsis* page 40
1d Lower surface of gills
      3a Substance woody   *Lenzites* page 40
      3b Substance soft or tough but not woody
            Schizophyllum, Panellus, Pleurotus, Crepidotus pages 46-48

Sub-section 2 Gill fungi or agarics.
1a Fungus producing milk (white, watery or coloured) when broken.
      2a Stem fleshy, thick or thickish   *Lactarius* page 48
      2b Stem cartilaginous, thin   *Mycena* page 88
1b Fungus not producing milk on breaking.
      3a Fungus, especially gills, brittle   *Russula* page 54
      3b ↓ Fungus waxy-looking, gills narrow wedge-shaped in cross-
            section   *Hygrophorus* page 62
      3c Fungus neither brittle nor waxy in appearance.
            4a Spores white or pale coloured   see page 66
            4b Spores dirty pinkish to dull pinkish cinnamon   see page 94
            4c Spores bright rusty brown   see page 96
            4d Spores dull (cigar) brown   see page 104
            4e Spores dark brown with violet or chocolate tint   see page 108
            4f Spores black or greeny grey   see page 114

Ascomycetes Spore-shooting fungi

These fungi are distinguished by possessing asci from which the spores are shot out to a considerable distance (see page 8). In the field they are recognized by their smooth spore-bearing surfaces being directed predominantly upwards and by the distinctive shapes of the fruit-body: a flat crust, a disc, saucer or cup, a convoluted mass, an erect club or antler-like growth or a variously shaped head carried on a stalk. Such shapes are rarely seen in the Basidiomycetes, but the club or antler-like fruit-body also occurs in fairy clubs (page 30) and the 'jelly fungi' (page 20). The convoluted mass, the disc and the saucer shape are also found in the latter but the only Ascomycetes in which they are also gelatinous are *Ascocoryne* and *Bulgaria* (see below).

Discomycetes

These differ from the Pyrenomycetes (see page 18) by not having perithecia and the surface of the fruit-body not being minutely pimpled.

Bulgaria inquinans Batchelor's or Pope's Buttons. Fruit-bodies up to 3—4cm across, with a gelatinous-rubbery consistency, often clustered together, like thick buttons with strongly convex lower surfaces; margins curved inwards at first, shining black and smooth on top, dark brown and scurfy below. Occurs on logs and branches of oak, less frequently beech or other trees, October to November; common. The rather similar *Exidia plana* (page 22) has a pimply instead of smooth spore-bearing surface.

Aleuria (*Peziza, Otidia*) *aurantia* Orange Peel Fungus. Fruit-bodies around 2—4cm or up to 10cm across, gregarious, flat to cup-shaped, circular to variously splitting or lobed, bright orange; whitish and minutely downy underneath; flesh brittle. Occurs on bare soil or even raw clay or gravel; September to January; frequent. *Melastiza chateri* could be mistaken for *Aleuria aurantia* but it is smaller (up to around 1·5cm across), more regular in outline and has minute, brown hairs on the underneath surface towards the margin.

Peziza Elf-cups. A large genus of saucer to cup-shaped fungi; many species are difficult to name without a microscope.

Peziza vesiculosa Bladder Elf-cup. Fruit-bodies at first globose with apical opening, later cup- or bowl-shaped, 2—5cm across or more, palish yellow-brown, often clustered; margin often shallowly notched. Occurs on manure heaps, old straw-bales and other heavily manured places; September to April; fairly common. See fig. 1 for a diagram of the fruit-body structure. *P. repanda* is very similar, but less yellowish brown; fruit-body shallower and more saucer-shaped; fairly common in woods. *P. succosa* is recognized by a scanty yellow milk produced when broken. *P. badia* is dark brown inside, paler outside. *Rhizina undulata*, the Pine Fire-fungus, is rather similar to a *Peziza* in form but the fruit-body is flat, often undulating, dark brown to blackish, and attached to the ground by numerous root-like structures. Common in coniferous woods and often associated with fires.

Chlorosplenium (*Chlorociboria*) *aeruginascens*. Fruit-bodies around 5—10mm across, blue-green or, sometimes, yellowish, shallow cup-shaped to flat, with a short, slender stalk; gregarious. On dead wood of broad-leaved trees, especially oak. The wood is stained green and sometimes is used for carving into small ornaments. September to October; stained wood common, fruit-bodies found only occasionally.

Bulgaria inquinans

Aleuria aurantia

Peziza vesiculosa

Chlorosplenium aeruginascens

Ascocoryne (*Coryne*) *sarcoides* Fruit-body gelatinous, mauve to dull lilac, often with a pinkish or rosy tinge, at first a brain-like to irregularly lobed mass, later with somewhat cup-shaped, sessile or shortly stalked components, from 2—10mm across, producing both conidia and ascospores. Occurs on dead wood especially beech; August to December; common. *A. cylichnium* is very similar and can only be distinguished microscopically.

The earth tongues are species of *Geoglossum*, *Trichoglossum* and *Microglossum* that resemble the fairy clubs (page 30) in having a club-shaped fruit-body 2—6cm high, but differ in being black or in *M. viride* dark green. Occur on lawns and grassland, or in woods (*M. viride*); uncommon.

Leotia lubrica Gum-drop Fungus. Fruit-bodies 1—5cm high, gelatinous and slimy, often clustered, with a small, brownish olive head, 0·5—1cm across, which is rolled inwards underneath, and often somewhat lobed. Stalk 3—10mm thick, ochre or amber, dotted with small greenish granules; cylindrical and straight, or curved towards the base. Occurs in broad-leaved woods and under bracken, often in wettish places, common. *Mitrula paludosa*, the Brook or Bog Beacon, is somewhat similar, but has a club-shaped, orange-yellow head and white stalk. Occurs on rotting leaves and sticks in ditches and streamlets; April to July; common.

Helvella crispa Common White Helvella or False Morel †. Fruit-body 4—10cm high, with a head consisting of a more or less horizontal sheet of tissue which is wavy to crisped, somewhat irregularly lobed, often convoluted, rather thin, whitish to cream-coloured. Head supported on a white, irregularly and strongly ribbed, hollow stem, 2—3cm wide, often wider towards the base, the flesh having many small cavities. Poisonous when raw, said to be edible cooked but reported at times to cause illness. Occurs in broad-leaved woods; August to November; common, rarely also March to April. *H. lacunosa* is very similar, but grey with a dark grey cap.

Morchella esculenta Common Morel **. Fruit-body 8—20cm high. Head 4—12cm long, ovoid, consisting of a honeycomb-like mass of shallow, irregular, angular pits, ochreous to yellowish brown. Stalk white to cream, cylindrical or slightly wider at base, brittle and hollow; surface even or shallowly longitudinally furrowed, smooth or minutely scurfy. Occurs in broad-leaved woods, hedgerows, banks or in open grassland, in rich, often disturbed soil; April to May, widespread but usually uncommon and often solitary or only a few together. A highly esteemed, edible fungus. Separated into several different species by some authorities, but others consider these variants of the single species. *M. vulgaris*, the form illustrated, is distinguished by the ridges on the head being rounded, whereas in *M. esculenta* they are sharp-edged. *M. elata* * has a conical head with dark brown, longitudinal ridges connected by short horizontal ones; it is a distinct and uncommon species. *Mitrophora semilibera* * has a similar but shorter head, which is free from the stem at the lower margin instead of fused with it as in *Morchella*. *Gyromitra esculenta* †, the Turban Fungus or Lorchel, resembles a *Morchella* but the fawn to chestnut brown head is brain-like and not honey-combed. As with *Helvella crispa* it is poisonous when raw and can cause symptoms of poisoning if handled in large quantities, but is edible when cooked. Occurs under conifers on sandy soils in April; fairly frequent in northern Europe including Scotland.

*Ascocoryne
sarcoides*

left
Leotia lubrica
right
Helvella crispa

*Morchella
esculenta*

Pyrenomycetes Flask fungi

Recognized by the minute pimples on the surface of the fruit-bodies which are the mouths of the flask-shaped spore-producing cavities (perithecia). These may be seen if the fruit-body is cut open. The fruit-bodies are hard, black and charcoal-like in the species illustrated, but in others they are soft and brightly coloured as in the rather uncommon but very interesting genus *Cordyceps. C. militaris*, the Scarlet Caterpillar Fungus, grows in the living tissues of caterpillars. When these pupate in the ground, a club-shaped, orange fruit-body grows up and appears above the soil. *C. ophioglossoides* has a club-shaped head, yellowish at first, becoming blackish later, with a yellowish stem. It grows parasitically on a subterranean tuber-like fungus of the genus *Elaphomyces. Ustulina deusta*, one of the group with charcoal-like flesh, forms a thick, flattish crust and is commonly found on stumps, mainly of beech, and the roots radiating from them. It is greyish white when young and producing conidia, but is black and brittle later.

Hypoxylon fragilforme (*H. coccineum*) Red Wood-wart Fungus. Fruit-bodies subglobose, up to 1cm across, at first pink to brick-red, becoming darker; surface pimply. Gregarious on logs, especially beech, very common. *H. fuscum* is similar but with smaller fruit-bodies up to 4mm across and purplish brown to purplish grey; sometimes it forms a continuous crust. Very common on hazel and alder wood. Both species occur throughout the year.

Daldinia concentrica Cramp Balls or King Alfred's Cakes. Fruit-body hemi-spherical to subglobose, 3—6cm across, at first dark reddish brown then somewhat shiny and black, smooth apart from minute pimples, the flesh grey with numerous concentric dark zones. Solitary or in groups, very common on dead broad-leaved trees, logs and branches, especially of ash. Occurs in all months. The name 'Cramp Balls' refers to an old country custom of carrying the fruit-bodies in a pocket to ward off cramp.

Xylaria polymorpha Dead-men's Fingers. Fruit-body club-shaped, sometimes grooved or with irregularities, 3—8cm high, 1·5—2·5cm wide, surface minutely pimpled, black; with a short black, cylindrical stem; flesh white with a black crust. Occurs singly or in clusters at the bases of dead stumps of broad-leaved trees, especially beech; throughout the year; common. The structure of the fruit-body is shown in fig. 2.

Xylaria hypoxylon Candle-snuff or Stag's Horn Fungus. Fruit-body varying from a simple erect, often flattened stem to a much branched antler-shape; at first white with powdery conidia above and black below; finally entirely black and covered with prominant pimples (the mouths of the perithecia). Very common on dead wood in late autumn but occurs the whole year round.

Tuberales

Globose or subglobose subterranean fungi with internal spore-producing tissue. Rarely seen unless specially searched for. *Tuber melanosporum* is the Périgord Truffle of the gourmets and occurs in southern Europe. The English Truffle, *T. aestivum*, was formerly collected in beech woods in southern England and was highly esteemed. Both species have hard knobbly surfaces and the flesh is dark brown with a network of whitish veins, the first being 2—8cm across and the second 1—3cm.

Hypoxylon
fragiforme

Daldinia
concentrica

Xylaria
polymorpha

Xylaria hypoxylon

Basidiomycetes Spore-dropping fungi

Fungi belonging to this group are characterized by the spores being produced on basidia (see page 8) and in consequence, with the exception of the Gasteromycetales (stomach fungi), in still air the spores fall vertically and are deposited directly below the surfaces that produce them. As a result these surfaces predominantly face downwards or sideways, a characteristic by which the group may be recognized in the field.

Jelly fungi

The basic characteristic by which this group is distinguished is the possession of special types of basidium which are variously lobed or divided, but this is constantly associated with gelatinous flesh, a character possessed by very few fungi belonging to other groups, notably *Ascocoryne*, *Bulgaria* and *Leotia* in the Ascomycetes (page 14), *Merulius tremellosus* (page 24) and *Fistulina* (page 34) in the Polypores and *Rhodotus palmatus*, an uncommon pink-spored agaric. Although a small group, the genera show a wide range of shape.

Dacrymyces stillatus (*D. deliquescens*) Fruit-bodies gelatinous, vary from individual, yellow or orange-yellow, sometimes wrinkled, cushions 1—5mm across, to confluent masses of cushions up to 20mm long. Conidia are formed at first and the fruit-bodies are then orange. Occurs on dead and especially worked wood of all sorts; very common in wet weather throughout the year.

Calocera cornea Fruit-bodies gelatinous, awl-shaped or narrowly club-shaped, unbranched or very sparsely branched above, round in cross-section, 4—15mm high, 0·5—1mm thick, pale yellow. Scattered to gregarious, usually two to three clustered together. Occurs on dead wood of broad-leaved trees; throughout the year; common.

Calocera viscosa Jelly-antler Fungus Fruit-bodies 1—10cm high, gelatinous, orange-yellow and slimy to the touch, antler-shaped, being repeatedly forked into two from the base; the branches equal and occurring at shorter intervals towards the top, rounded in cross-section or sometimes slightly flattened; base white tomentose; rooting. Occurs on dead coniferous wood; September to April; common. This and the previous species could be mistaken for fairy club fungi but these are never gelatinous.

Tremella mesenterica Yellow Brain Fungus. Fruit-body gelatinous, forming contorted brain-like masses, the folds sometimes flattened, often longer than broad, 1—10cm by 1—5cm, golden yellow to orange. Occurs on dead branches of broad-leaved trees and bushes including gorse; throughout the year but especially November to December, common.

Pseudohydnum (*Tremellodon*) *gelatinosum*, the Jelly Hedgehog Fungus, resembles the non-gelatinous Hedgehog Fungi (*Hydnum*) in possessing a cap with spines underneath. It is bluish or brownish grey, 2—6cm across and often has a short lateral stem. Occurs on pine stumps and on the ground under pines; September to December; occasional.

Dacrymyces
stillatus

Calocera cornea

left
Calocera viscosa
right
Tremella
mesenterica

Exidia plana (*E. glandulosa* of many authors) Witches' Butter. Fruit-bodies gelatinous often clustered, rounded to disc-shaped, 2—5cm across, shortly stalked or stalkless, often later becoming contorted and brain-like, gelatinous, black, somewhat woolly underneath (i.e. towards the support), with numerous conical wart-like protruberances above, but smooth between these. Occurs on dead wood of broad-leaved trees: stumps, logs or branches; frequent. See under *Bulgaria inquinans* (page 14) for the distinguishing features of this very similar fungus.

E. thuretiana has opalescent white, disc-shaped to shallowly lobed fruit-bodies that may form somewhat brain-like patches 0·5—4cm across; grows on dead branches of broad-leaved trees; frequent in winter.

Auricularia mesenterica Tripe Fungus. Fruit-body gelatinous, at first rounded and cup-shaped, then spreading laterally to form a resupinate sheet of tissue with the upper margin growing outwards to form a shelf or bracket up to 4cm wide, with a thick, rounded and bluntly lobed margin. Top of the bracket dark brown, brownish grey, or ashy, with darker banding, the underneath surface pale grey, later reddish to dark dull purple with a whitish bloom; veined, often prominently so. Fruit-bodies soon confluent, covering areas up to a metre or more long with numerous projecting brackets. Occurs on stumps or logs of broad-leaved trees; throughout the year; common.

Hirneola auricula-judae (*Auricularia auricula* or *A. auricula-judae*) Jew's Ear *. Fruit-body gelatinous, cup- to ear-shaped, often more broad than high, the concave surface facing downwards, 3—8cm across, red-brown to olive-brown; upper surface velvety, lower surface with a greyish bloom, often with prominent, though sparse, veins or ridges. Occurs on dead elder branches, occasionally on other broad-leaved trees; throughout the year; very common. In the illustration, the underneath surface is facing the camera.

Aphyllophorales

This group includes all the remaining Basidiomycetes that produce their spores on a freely exposed surface of the fruit-body except for the boletes or sponge-caps and the agarics which produce them in soft, spongy tubes or on gills respectively. The spore-bearing surface may be smooth, wrinkled, veined, warted, spiny or consist of tubes. A few have gill-like plates, but these are distinguished from the agarics by their tough or woody consistency.

Fungi with the spore-bearing surfaces not tubular

Crust-like fungi

A considerable number of Basidiomycetes are resupinate, i.e. they form simple crusts on the surface on which they grow. Although they often have interesting microscopic structures the species are mostly difficult or impossible to recognize without the aid of a microscope, so only a few will be described, as examples, in this book.

Hyphodontia sambuci (Corticium sambuci or *C. serum*). Forms snow or chalk white, very thin, whitewash-like patches with a finely granular surface on dead branches of broad-leaved trees, especially elder on which it is very common. Occurs throughout the year but mainly in autumn and winter.

Exidia plana

Auricularia mesenterica

Hirneola auricula-judae

Hyphodontia sambuci

Vuilleminia (*Corticium*) *comedens*. Forms a thin, flesh-coloured to dingy lilac, resupinate crust which is smooth and slightly sticky. Occurs underneath thin bark on dead branches of broad-leaved trees, especially oak and hazel. The bark splits open and rolls back revealing the fungus and this behaviour of the bark is a useful characteristic by which the fungus may be identified.

Pulcherricium (*Corticium*) *caeruleum* is a fairly uncommon, resupinate fungus that is easily recognized by its beautiful azure blue colour. It grows on dead branches of broad-leaved trees.

Peniophora lycii (*P. caesia*) forms grey, lilac or pale grey crusts with smooth surfaces on dead branches. There are several other similarly coloured species: *P. quercina* and *P. cinerea* are common and can only be identified with certainty by microscopic examination. *P. incarnata* is a bright salmon-pink and not uncommon. The genus *Peniophora* in the narrow sense, is distinguished from all other resupinate fungi by the spore deposit being dull pink.

Phlebia merismoides (*P. aurantiaca, P. radiata*). Fruit-bodies with thickish flesh (2—3mm) forming somewhat irregular, round to oval patches up to 8—10cm across, varying from whitish or pale flesh-coloured to dull purplish with the margin orange-coloured and fringed; sometimes entirely orange. Surface variously wrinkled or tubercular, or with short to long ridges which may radiate from the centre. Flesh somewhat gelatinous, with a waxy appearance. Occurs on dead stumps, logs and branches of broad-leaved trees. Common in late autumn and winter. *P. aurantiaca* (*radiata*) was once considered a separate species.

Bracket fungi

Only those without tubes or gills are dealt with here. For those that have tubes see under polypores on page 32.

Merulius tremellosus. Fruit-body, at first, consisting of spreading, resupinate sheets with the upper edges growing outwards to form well-developed brackets 2·5—15cm long and projecting 1—4cm, often in tiers, gelatinous but fairly tough; somewhat translucent. Upper surface of bracket whitish and woolly, the margin toothed or fringed and often pinkish. Surface of the sheets and lower surface of bracket orange-buff or pinkish with a prominent network of blunt-edged veins, folds and ridges forming well-marked, irregular, shallow pores. Occurs on stumps and logs of broad-leaved trees; August to February; fairly frequent.

M. corium (*M. papyrinus, Byssomerulius corium*) has a similar type of spore-bearing surface, though on a smaller scale. Initially the surface is smooth, then it develops a network of very shallow folds and small, rounded warts to give an appearance of small, very shallow, irregular pores, pale buff to flesh coloured. The fruit-body starts as a thin, leathery, resupinate crust of rounded patches which unite to form a continuous sheet 20—50cm long. The upper margins grow outwards to form narrow shelves, whose upper surfaces are whitish, hairy and sometimes indistinctly, concentrically banded. Occurs on dead wood of logs and fallen branches of broad-leaved trees; throughout the year; frequent.

Vuilleminia comedens

Peniophora lycii

Phlebia merismoides

Merulius tremellosus

Chondrostereum (***Stereum***) ***purpureum***. Purple Stereum or Silver-leaf Fungus. Forms spreading, resupinate, leathery crusts whose upper edges may turn outwards to form more or less well-developed brackets, often in tiers and projecting up to 5cm; margins often, more or less, lobed and crisped. Surfaces of crusts and lower surfaces of brackets lilac to purplish when fresh, later discolouring brownish, smooth. Upper surfaces of brackets whitish to greyish, or brownish, woolly or hairy, sometimes banded. Occurs on dead branches, logs and stumps of broad-leaved trees; throughout the year especially in autumn; common. It is the cause of a serious disease of plums and other trees in which the leaves assume a silvery appearance from which it gets the name 'Silver-leaf' disease.

Stereum hirsutum Yellow Stereum. Forms spreading, resupinate, leathery crusts whose upper edges soon turn outwards to form well-developed brackets, often in tiers, projecting 2—8cm; the margins often wavy and lobed. At times the resupinate portion may predominate, at others it is almost absent. Surfaces of crusts and lower surfaces of brackets bright ochre-yellow to egg-yellow, becoming dull buff with age, smooth. Upper surfaces of brackets densely hairy with rigid, shortish hairs, ochre to greyish, more or less banded. Occurs on dead branches, logs, stumps, etc. of broad-leaved trees, throughout the year; very common, amongst the most frequently encountered of larger fungi.

Stereum gausapatum (*S. spadiceum* of some writers). Fruit-bodies produce spreading, leathery crusts whose upper margins often turn outwards to form brackets up to 5cm wide, often in tiers; margins often waved, crisped or lobed, at first white. Surfaces of crusts and lower surfaces of brackets dingy brown to dark chestnut-brown, smooth, bleeding a blood-coloured juice if cut or bruised. Tops of brackets bay to greyish-brown, hairy. Occurs on stumps and fallen branches of broad-leaved trees, especially oak; throughout the year; frequent. Causes a serious heart-rot of oak trees. Photographed from above but with one fruit-body turned over.

Stereum sanguiholentum is similar but occurs on coniferous wood. The tops of the brackets are pallid whitish and the underneath surfaces greyish to brownish black. *S. rugosum* also bleeds when cut but is usually completely resupinate, rather thick, uneven and pinkish buff. It occurs on the wood of broad-leaved trees. *Corticium evolvens* (*laeve*) resembles a *Stereum* but the flesh is thinner and lacks the distinct layers found in this genus. It is mainly resupinate but the upper margin may turn out to form a narrow shelf; the surface is smooth, cream, flesh-coloured or pale buffy brown. It is very common in late autumn and winter on dead branches, logs, etc., of broad-leaved trees.

Hymenochaete rubiginosa. Fruit-bodies form brackets 1—4cm wide, deep rust-brown becoming date-brown to blackish, at first velvety and often concentrically banded on top, rather hard and rigid and with a resupinate portion; margins yellowish, often wavy. Lower surfaces dark rust-brown, smooth. Occurs on stumps and dead branches of broad-leaved trees; throughout the year; fairly common.

Chondrostereum purpureum

Stereum hirsutum

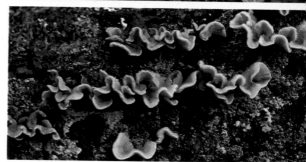

Stereum gausapatum

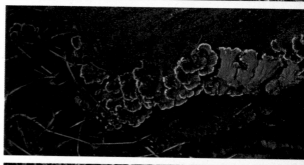

Hymenochaete rubiginosa

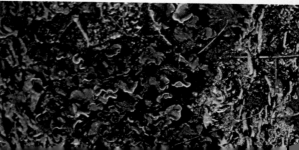

Thelephora (*Phylacteria*) *terrestris* Earth Fan. Fruit-bodies from more or less erect to almost horizontal, fan-shaped, sometimes curved and concentrically arranged and then may simulate a single funnel-shaped fruit-body, leathery, tough and fibrous. Upper surfaces chocolate-brown to blackish, rough with radially arranged coarse fibres; margin paler and fringed. Lower surfaces violet-grey, wrinkled or slightly pimply. Spore deposit dull dark brown, and this distinguishes the genus *Thelephora* from *Stereum* which has white spores. Occurs on sandy ground under pines or on heaths; August to December; fairly common. Photographed from above.

Fungi with stems but not having tubes or gills

Craterellus cornucopoides Horn-of-Plenty **. Fruit-body narrowly and deeply funnel-shaped, 3—8cm across, 5—10cm high, the tube of the funnel descending to the base of the fungus and the rim curving out, round and down, often waved and crisped. Upper surface brownish black to blackish when moist, drying palish sepia, often with small scales; lower surface of the more spreading part of the funnel ash-grey, smooth at first then wrinkled, below this blackish. Flesh thin, leathery. Occurs amongst dead leaves in broad-leaved woods especially of beech, often in troops; September to November; frequent.

Cantharellus infundibuliformis Funnel Chantarelle *. Similar in shape to the last species but with a distinct cap and stem, 4—8cm high. Cap convex at first, later umbilicate to funnel-shaped, 2—5cm across, dark brown when moist, becoming yellowish brown as it dries. Upper surface smooth; margin often lobed and crisped and convex. Lower surface at first yellow later grey, with irregularly branched, pronounced, blunt, lengthwise ridges or folds which run down to the top of the stem and resemble very shallow gills. Stem 2—7cm× 3—8mm, deep yellow, often grooved or flattened and slightly swollen at the base, smooth, hollow, the cavity sometimes connected through a perforation with the bottom of the cap funnel. Fruit-bodies sometimes clustered, on the ground in broad-leaved and coniferous woods; June to December; fairly frequent. *Var. lutescens* is entirely yellow. *C. tubaeformis* which differs in having a tawny stem and more elliptically-shaped spores, is considered a mere form of *C. infundibuliformis* by some, but a separate species by others.

Cantharellus cibarius Chantarelle **. Fruit-body 4—7cm high, entirely egg-yellow. Cap 3—10cm across, funnel-shaped in outline, the top slightly convex at first then flat or with a shallow depression; margin incurved at first, often waved and lobed. The lower surface of the cap has blunt, shallow, branching, gill-like ribs running down to the top of the stem, which is short, 3—5cm× 1—2cm, cylindrical, straight or curved, smooth and solid. Odour suggests apricots. Many often occur together on the ground in broad-leaved woods especially of beech or oak; June to November; common. A well-known and highly esteemed edible species. The flavour is quite different from that of the common mushroom and is perhaps something of an acquired taste. Methods of cooking other than frying should be employed. *Hygrophoropsis aurantiaca*, the False Chantarelle * (page 86) is similar but does not smell of apricots and has true, plate-like though narrow gills and is associated with conifers. Its spores turn red-brown with iodine solutions, whereas those of *Cantharellus cibarius* do not.

*Thelephora
terrestris*

*Craterellus
cornucopioides*

*Cantharellus
infundibuliformis*

*Cantharellus
cibarius*

Hydnum repandum Common Hedgehog Fungus **. Fruit-body stalked, flesh rather dry, breaking easily. Cap 5—8cm across, shallow convex to flattish but often waved and somewhat irregular, palish buff, thick fleshed. Surface smooth with an incurved margin. Lower surface thickly covered with brittle, pale buff, awl-shaped spines of varying length, 2—5mm long, slightly decurrent onto the top of the stem. Stem white, ochre towards the base, central or attached towards one side of the cap, short, 3—8cm × 2—4cm. Taste bitter (when raw). Occurs on the ground in broad-leaved woods, at times in rings or arcs; August to November; fairly common. *H. rufescens*, considered a mere colour variant by some, differs in having a more red-brown colour. There are several other species of 'cap and stalk' fungi with spines that belong to other genera, but none are common. The most frequent is *Hydnellum velutinum* which has a rust-coloured, concentrically banded, funnel-shaped, velvety, leathery and tough cap and brown spines. Occurs on sandy ground in both broad-leaved and coniferous woods.

Auriscalpium vulgare has a small brown cap, 1—3cm across with a long stem attached to one side; it grows on pine-cones. Resupinate fungi with spines also occur, notably *Mycoacia uda* in which they are yellow. All these fungi were once placed in the genus *Hydnum*.

Clavariaceae or fairy clubs.

This group is characterized by the erect, narrowly club-shaped to much branched, bush or tree-like, non-gelatinous fruit-bodies; the spores are produced all over their smooth surfaces. Fungi with similar shapes are also found amongst the 'jelly fungi' (page 20) and some Ascomycetes (page 14).

Clavariadelphus (*Clavaria*) *pistillaris* Giant Fairy Club *. Fruit-body a simple, broad or pestle-shaped club 7—30cm high and 2—5cm wide, yellowish buff, becoming brownish especially in the lower part, minutely velvety, often wrinkled, dimpled or broadly furrowed. Flesh inside soft and loose. Spore deposit ochre. Occurs on the ground, singly or in small groups, in broad-leaved woods; September to December; occasional. The largest of the fairy clubs.

Clavariopsis (*Clavaria*) *helvola* (*C. inaequalis*). Fruit-body a simple, narrow club, broadest and rounded, and occasionally bluntly branched at the top, 2·5—8cm high, bright or orange-yellow, cylindrical or slightly flattened. Occurs singly or in small groups in grass in woods, grassland or lawns; September to December; frequent. There are several rather similar yellow species. *C. fusiformis*, Golden Spindles, differs in being narrow spindle-shaped and tufted. *C. pulchra* is also spindle-shaped but not tufted and is darker orange, often brownish at the tips. *C. luteoalba* is apricot coloured. *Clavaria vermicularis*, White Spindles, is narrow spindle-shaped, densely tufted and white, whilst *C. fumosa* is similar but grey. All grow in grassy places.

Clavulina (*Clavaria*) *cristata* Crested Fairy Club. Fruit-body 3—8cm high, pure to slightly pinkish or greyish white, irregularly branched, often densely so and appearing like a minute bush, the branches flattened upwards, the ultimate branchlets often sharp pointed giving a crested appearance. Occurs on the ground in broad-leaved woods; June to December; common. *C. cinerea* is similar but grey. *C. rugosa*, Wrinkled Club, is also similar but less branched and the branches thicken upwards, have lengthwise wrinkles and blunt apices.

Hydnum repandum

Clavariadelphus pistillaris

Clavariopsis helvola

Clavulina cristata

Ramaria Distinguished from other fairy clubs by the ochre spore deposit. All species are much branched.

Ramaria (Clavaria) stricta Fruit-bodies 5–10cm high, densely branched from the base, the branches parallel, cylindrical and irregularly forked, fragile, pinkish buff with pale yellow branchlets; base tinged a dull wine colour. Taste bitter. Odour sometimes spicy. Occurs on or near rotten wood or old stumps, the only fairy club that grows on wood; August to January; frequent. *R. formosa* † is somewhat similar but has pinkish buff, orange-rose or pinkish ochre branches with lemon-yellow tips; base whitish. Taste bitter, very bitter when cooked and causing diarrhoea if eaten. On the ground in broad-leaved woods; occasional. *R. aurea* * is a massive species, 5–12cm high, 10–20cm wide, entirely ochre to egg-yellow. Occurs on the ground in both coniferous and broad-leaved woods; frequent in mainland Europe, uncommon in Britain. *Clavariopsis corniculata* is like a small, egg-yellow *Ramaria* but occurs in grassland and has white spores. *Calocera viscosa* is similar but gelatinous (see page 20).

Sparassis crispa Cauliflower Fungus **. Fruit-body cauliflower-like, globose, 10–60cm across, consisting of an intricate mass of strongly flattened, pale buff branches. Occurs on or near pine stumps; September to November; occasional.

Polypores

This group includes all fungi whose spore-bearing surfaces consist of tubes, the mouths of which appear as pores, with the exception of the boletes or sponge caps which have soft tubes underneath a cap on a central stem and belong to the Agaricales. A few polypores have gill-like plates but these differ from the gills of the agarics by their woody or leathery consistency. The arrangement of the species in this book is as follows:

Schizopora paradoxa (*Poria vaporaria, P. mucida, Xylodon versiporus, Irpex obliquus*). Fruit-body a spreading white to very pale ochre crust covered with irregular, angular pores, 0·2–1mm across, 1–2mm deep, often torn to form labyrinths or plate-like teeth. Occurs on all types of dead wood throughout the year; very common. Amongst other white, resupinate polypores, *Rigidoporus sanguinolentus* may be recognized by its turning red on bruising.

Phellinus ferruginosus Forms a hard, corky, spreading crust up to 30cm long and 10cm wide which is dull rusty brown in colour. Pores rounded, 0·12–0·15mm across, tubes up to 2mm long, sometimes in layers since the fungus persists for several seasons. Occurs on dead branches; common. *P. ferreus* only differs in having longer spores.

Ramaria stricta

Sparassis crispa

*Schizopora
paradoxa*

*Phellinus
ferruginosus*

Fistulina hepatica Beefsteak Fungus *. Fruit-body a rounded, semicircular to tongue-shaped, 2—3cm thick bracket, 10—25cm across, sometimes with a short stalk-like base, blood-red to liver-coloured; the upper surface rough. Pores round, pale flesh coloured, the tubes separate from each other if the surface is flexed. Flesh red, rather fibrous, yielding a reddish juice; the surface layer gelatinous. Spore deposit pinkish brown. Occurs on trunks of living oaks or occasionally other trees, causing the wood to turn rich brown before decaying: the so-called 'Brown Oak' disease. August to November; fairly common. Best cooked as cubes added to stews when it has a pleasant acid flavour.

Tyromyces (*Leptoporus, Polyporus*) *caesius* Forms roughly semicircular, thickish brackets, 2—8cm across, often in tiers, sometimes partly resupinate. Brackets white, later bluish grey, soft and woolly or shaggy above, later smooth. Tubes white, 3—9mm long; pores white becoming bluish grey if bruised, round or oblong, 0·15 to 0·30mm across, becoming torn. Flesh rather soft, white and watery, sometimes tinged blue on cutting. Spore powder bluish. Occurs on dead stumps and branches of broad-leaved or, more especially, of coniferous trees; throughout the year but mainly in autumn; frequent. There are several other white or whitish species of *Tyromyces*. *T. lacteus* is very similar to the above, but is entirely white and does not bruise bluish. *T. stipticus* is also white with the margin becoming rusty and differs from the other species in having a bitter taste; it occurs on coniferous wood.

Laetiporus (*Grifola, Polyporus*) *sulphureus* Sulphur Polypore *. Produces bracket to flap-shaped, sometimes wavy caps 10—30cm across and up to 5cm thick, often in tiers from a common, massive, tuber-like base. Fruit-body when fresh orange with a sulphur-yellow margin, becoming paler and duller in colour with age or on drying; surface like wash-leather. Flesh thick and soft but fibrous and cheesy-crumby. Tubes up to 4mm long, pores small, round, 0·3—0·8mm across, bright sulphur-yellow. Occurs on stumps and trunks of broad-leaved and coniferous trees; May to November; frequent. Causes a serious red-brown rot of the heart wood.

Meripilus (*Grifola, Polyporus*) *giganteus* Giant Polypore. Forms dense tufts of overlapping, often concentrically arranged, fan-shaped caps growing from a tuber-like mass at the base, the whole being up to 1 metre across; the individual caps 10—30cm wide and up to 2cm thick, gradually narrowing downwards to stem-like bases, yellow-brown to date brown, sometimes faintly banded; surfaces granular or scurfy; margins creamy to yellowish, wavy or lobed. Tubes white, 1—2mm long; pores whitish, blackish when bruised. Flesh fibrous and somewhat tough but breaking easily, blackening on cutting. Occurs near stumps or the bases of broad-leaved trees, especially beech and oak; July to January; fairly common. *Grifola* (*Polyporus*) *frondosa* * is somewhat similar but the caps are smaller, up to 4cm across, are greyish or smoky brown and carried on branching stems. It has a rancid odour reminiscent of mice and the flesh and pores do not blacken. Edible when young but tough. Occurs at the bases of broad-leaved trees and stumps; September to October; occasional.

Fistulina hepatica

Tyromyces caesius

Laetiporus sulphureus

Meripilus giganteus

Polyporus squamosus Dryad's Saddle. Caps 10–60cm across, 1–4cm thick, horizontal, semi-circular or kidney-shaped to fan-shaped or sometimes nearly to completely circular and funnel-shaped, often several together one above the other; surfaces ochre-yellowish with numerous dark brown, flattened, feather-like, concentrically arranged scales; flesh soft but fibrous. Tubes up to 7mm long, running down the stem; pores white to cream, 1–2mm across, angular and honeycomb-like, torn at the edge. Stem attached towards or at the margin of the cap, sometimes almost non-existent but can be up to 5cm long and 1–5cm thick, pale above, brown to black below. Occurs on stumps and trunks of broad-leaved, often living, trees, especially elms; April to December; fairly common. *P. ciliatus* (*Polyporellus, Leucoporus brumalis*) has a convex to umbilicate, yellowish to deep brown cap, 2–5cm across, smooth with a downy margin; pores minute, 0·04–0·2mm across, round and white, running down the stem; stem often central, 6cm×2–6mm, light to greyish brown. Occurs on dead wood; September to May; frequent.

Piptoporus (*Polyporus, Ungulina*) *betulinus* Razor-strop Fungus or Birch Polypore. Cap thick, soft and bun-like, semicircular to kidney- or hoof-shaped, sometimes almost circular, stemless and broadly to narrowly attached, 8–15cm across, 2–5cm thick with a thick rounded margin. Upper surface shallowly convex and smooth, with a thin greyish or very pale brownish, separable skin. Tubes up to 10mm long; pores small 0·15–0·25mm across, round and white. Flesh white, softly corky. Occurs on living and dead birch trunks, causing their death; summer and autumn; very common, dried specimens found at all times. The flesh was formerly cut into strips, mounted on wood and used for stropping razors. It has also been used by entomologists for mounting small insects.

Coriolus (*Trametes, Polystictus*) *versicolor* Many-zoned Polypore. Forms semi-circular, thin brackets, often in tiered rows. Upper surfaces often strongly velvety with rather rigid hairs, usually strongly concentrically banded with various colours which may include yellowish, brown, grey, brownish or greenish grey and black, some of the bands being smooth. Margins thin, paler coloured, often wavy or lobed. Tubes very short, up to 1mm deep. Pores white to cream, rounded to torn, 0·1–0·4mm across. Flesh thin (1–2mm), white and flexible, fibrous and tough. Occurs on dead wood of broad-leaved trees; throughout the year; very common.

Bjerkandera (*Gloeoporus, Leptoporus, Polyporus*) *adusta* Burnt Polypore. Fruit-bodies sometimes entirely resupinate crusts but usually the upper margins turning outwards to form well-developed, elongate to semi-circular brackets up to 4cm across, often in tiers, and frequently occurring in large numbers. Upper surfaces of brackets at first white to cream, later fawn, greyish fawn or blackish especially along the margin, sometimes faintly banded, finely velvety at first, later smooth. Tubes short, up to 2mm deep, grey to black and darker than the flesh above them; pores minute, 0·2–0·8mm across, round and smoke-grey, becoming blackish; absent towards the margin of the cap. Flesh thin, up to 6mm, whitish then grey, fibrous and flexible. Occurs on dead wood of trunks, stumps and branches of broad-leaved trees especially beech; throughout the year; common.

Polyporus squamosus

Piptoporus betulinus

Coriolus versicolor

Bjerkandera adusta

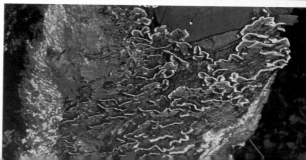

Hirschioporus (*Trichaptum, Coriolus, Trametes, Polystictus*) *abietinus* Fruit-bodies partly, rarely entirely, resupinate, usually with small, semi-circular caps 2cm across, but frequently united to form narrow shelves up to 4cm long and 2cm wide, often grouped together and tiered, thin 1—3mm, and flexible. Upper surface downy or velvety, concentrically banded, whitish to greyish. Margins tinged pink or lilac, thin, wavy or lobed. Tubes lilac, very short. Pores light violet, becoming light brownish to pale cocoa-brown, round or angular, 0·2—0·4mm across, becoming sinuous, torn or labyrinth-like. Flesh thin, tough, leathery and flexible, brownish or purplish. Occurs on dead wood of coniferous trees; throughout the year; fairly common. In the photograph the underneath surface of the central specimen is turned towards the camera.

Pseudotrametes (*Trametes*) *gibbosa* Cap a semi-circular to slightly elongate semi-circular, rigid bracket, 10—20cm across and 1—4cm thick where attached. Surface flat, whitish, creamy or more usually greyish, often tinted green by algal growth, concentrically banded by shallow furrows, downy or velvety; margin rounded. Tubes white, up to 15mm deep. Pores white, round or more usually longer than broad, 0·9—2·0mm×0·3—0·5mm and arranged with their lengths along the radii of the cap. Flesh white, corky and tough to rather hard. Occurs on dead wood especially stumps of beech on which it is common, rarely on other broad-leaved trees; in autumn and winter.

Ganoderma adspersum (*G. australe, G. europaeum*) Fruit-body a massive bracket, roughly and often irregularly semi-circular, somewhat hoof-like, 5—30cm across and up to 8cm thick; hard and woody. Upper surface red-brown to cinnamon, matt, flattish but lumpy and sometimes concentrically furrowed, with a distinct rigid crust that becomes very hard; margin thick and rounded. Tubes red-brown to cinnamon, sometimes in layers. Pores small, 0·15—0·25mm across, whitish at first, becoming brown when rubbed or with age. Flesh chestnut-brown to umber, fibrous, hard, up to 10cm thick and usually thicker than the tube layer. Spore powder cocoa-brown, often forming a thick, dusty covering to the tree or the ground below the fungus. Occurs on trunks of broad-leaved trees, mainly beeches; throughout the year; common, rarely on conifers. Absent from Scandinavia and Finland, where the very similar *G. applanatum* (a name formerly, commonly misapplied to the former fungus) replaces it, but becomes less frequent southwards. This species differs in being thinner, more flap-like, and having a sharper margin. Further the tube layer is thicker than the flesh above it; the spores are smaller. *G. lucidum* has a kidney-shaped cap with a lateral, knobbly stem. The fungus is recognized by being covered with a dark chestnut lacquer-like crust. Occurs on stumps of broad-leaved trees; rather rare.

Heterobasidion (*Formes, Ungulina*) *annosus* Forms a thickish, lumpy, woody mass, sometimes entirely resupinate, but usually with an irregularly wavy, bracket-shaped cap. Upper surface bright red-brown, blackish behind, often wrinkled and concentrically grooved, with a hard crust. Margin thinnish and white at first. Tubes in layers, each one around 1cm long, whitish; pores angular or irregular, 0·25—0·6mm across, white to pale cream; the surface they form is often irregular and has protuberances. Flesh white to creamy, corky-woody. Occurs on pine stumps and roots, especially where the latter are exposed by animal burrows; throughout the year, common.

Hirschioporus
abietinus

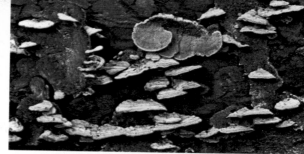

Pseudotrametes
gibbosa

Ganoderma
adspersum

Heterobasidion
annosus

Fomes fomentarius Tinder Fungus, is easily recognized by its strongly hoof-shaped, massive, fawn, grey or blackish, perennial fruit-bodies that occur on birch trees. Common in northern Europe and Scotland, but rare further south. *Phellinus (Fomes) igniarius* is somewhat similar but less strongly hoof-shaped and differs in having dark rusty instead of cinnamon or yellowish brown flesh and is found mainly on willows. *Phellinus pomaceus* resembles it but is more rounded and grows on plums, hawthorns and related trees. These three fungi are perennial, their tubes growing in successive layers one above another.

Daedaliopsis (Trametes, Daedalea) confragosa (*T. rubescens*) Reddenning Woody Polypore. Fruit-body a semi-circular, rigid bracket, 5—15cm across and up to 5cm thick. Upper surface smooth or radially wrinkled, at first whitish, then pale ochre, pale yellowish brown or palish umber, sometimes concentrically banded, finally often dark red to purplish brown next to the support. Tubes up to 12mm long. Pores angular 0·5—0·8mm across, often longer than wide, labyrinth-like or even with a tendency to form radially arranged plates, white then greyish in colour, becoming reddish when rubbed and turning violet with ammonia solution. Flesh up to 8mm thick, tough and corky, pale ochre then brown. Occurs on dead wood of broad-leaved trees, especially willows; throughout the year; fairly common.

Daedalea (Lenzites) quercina Mazegill. Fruit-body a semi-circular, sometimes almost hoof-shaped, bracket, up to 15cm wide, 10cm broad and 8cm thick, corky to woody, hard. Upper surface dull ochre, brownish or greyish, smooth or uneven, or with concentric banding and furrows, sometimes also radially wrinkled; margin blunt. Tubes (or plates) up to 4cm long. Pores near the cap margin longer than broad or sinuous, but further back mostly labyrinth-like to nearly gill-like, thick-walled, ochre buff. Flesh ochre-buff to pale red-brown, corky-woody. Occurs on oak stumps; throughout the year; common.

Lenzites betulina Fruit-bodies form flat, semi-circular brackets, 2—8cm across, 0·3—2·0cm thick, sometimes in tiers, occasionally with a resupinate portion. Surfaces white to greyish, concentrically banded; hairy or woolly; margins sometimes wavy. Spore-bearing surface of radiating and branching gill-like plates, up to 12mm broad, white to yellowish. Flesh thin, white and rather soft and flexible when fresh, later corky. Occurs on stumps and trunks of broad-leaved trees, especially birch; throughout the year; fairly common.

Coltricia (Xanthochrous, Polystictus, Polyporus) perennis Fruit-body centrally stalked. Cap funnel-shaped to umbilicate, 3—8cm across, concentrically banded tawny and rust brown, thin, leathery and finely velvety. Stem 2—7cm long and up to 10cm thick, deep rust-brown, velvety. Tubes up to 3mm deep, cinnamon, decurrent on to the stem. Pores ochre, rusty or dark brown, minute, 0·2—1·2mm across, angular to irregular. Flesh tawny brown, thin, fibrous and tough. Spore powder yellowish to yellow-brown. Occurs on sandy ground in woods and on heaths, especially where burnt; throughout the year; frequent. Differs from central-stemmed species of *Polyporus* (in the narrow sense) by the rusty instead of whitish flesh which turns dark blackish red-brown with caustic alkalis.

*Daedaliopsis
confragosa*

Daedalea quercina

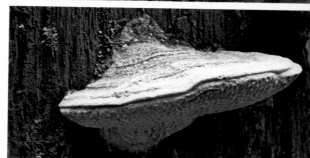

Lenzites betulina

Coltricia perennis

Agaricales

These fungi possess a spore-bearing surface consisting of tubes or gills. They differ from the Aphyllophorales in that the flesh is usually soft, decays rapidly and is never woody though in some it is slightly leathery and after drying out, it may be revived on wetting. These may be recognized as belonging to the Agaricales by their possessing true gills.

Boletes or sponge-caps

These have spongy tubes on the lower surface of a cap which is carried on a central stem. Members of four genera, *Boletus*, *Tylopilus*, *Suillus* and *Leccinum*, formerly included in the genus *Boletus*, are illustrated.

Boletus Cap surface not, or only, slightly sticky when wet. Stem not rough with dark scales, though sometimes granular or with a network. Spores olive-brown or rusty.

Boletus badius Bay Sponge-cap **. Cap 3—15cm across, bay brown or light chestnut, convex to flattened convex, slightly sticky when young, soon dry and smooth. Tubes lemon-yellow, turning blue-green on cutting. Pores angular, rather large, whitish at first then greeny yellow, blue-green when bruised. Stem 6—10cm×2—3cm, more or less cylindrical, brown, paler than the cap, slightly streaky. Flesh of cap and top of stem pale yellowish, bluish on cutting and this colour slowly fading. Occurs under conifers; August to November; common.

Boletus (*Xerocomus*) ***chrysenteron*** Red-cracking Sponge-cap *. Cap 3—10cm across, from deep purple or sooty brown to greyish fawn, convex then flattened; surface finely felted or velvety, often cracking and the flesh then often showing pink between the cracks. Pores sulphur- or lemon-yellow, finally dirty olive, large, angular, sometimes bruising bluish-green. Stem 4—8cm× 1—1·5cm, more or less cylindrical, lemon-chrome or lemon-yellow above, pink, scarlet or red from the middle downwards, with red or blood-red granules. Flesh cream to straw-coloured or lemon-yellow in the cap, browner in the stem, sometimes turning bluish. Occurs under broad-leaved trees; August to November; very common.

Boletus (*Xerocomus*) ***subtomentosus*** *. Very similar to the last, but there is no red colour on the stem nor between any cracks on the cap, also the pores remain bright gold-yellow instead of becoming olive. *B. lanatus* * is very similar but the pores turn blue rapidly on bruising, also the cap surface goes bluish to yellowish green with ammonia. *B. spadiceus* * differs by lacking this reaction but this species and *B. lanatus* have longitudinal veining with cross-connections on the stems, a characteristic not or only poorly shown in *B. subtomentosus*.

Boletus erythropus **. Cap 5—16cm across, bay, umber or snuff-brown with olive tints, flattened convex; surface smooth, slightly sticky in wet weather. Tubes lemon-yellow to greenish, turning dark blue on cutting. Pores round, small, orange-red to orange, bruising dark blue. Stem 5—14cm×2—5cm, cylindrical, base sometimes swollen, yellowish but densely dotted with orange-red to scarlet. Flesh yellow, immediately dark blue on cutting. Fairly common under broad-leaved trees but especially in coniferous woods; September to November. *B. luridus* ** is similar but differs in having a red network on the stem.

Boletus badius

Boletus chrysenteron

Boletus subtomentosus

Boletus erythropus

Boletus edulis Ceps or Cèpe **. Cap 6—20cm across, date-brown to bay, chestnut or dark brick, more or less flattened convex; margin whitish or with a white line; surface smooth to slightly rough, slightly sticky in wet weather. Tubes white, becoming greyish yellow, with small round, similarly coloured pores. Stem 3—23cm × 3—7cm, often rather robust, cylindrical to club-shaped or bulbous, light tawny or buff to whitish with a raised white network of veins usually confined to the upper half. Flesh white not turning blue. Occurs under broad-leaved or coniferous trees; August to November; common. A well-known and popular edible species, often used for making dried 'mushroom' soups. *B. aestivalis* (*reticulatus*) ** is very similar but usually has a paler coloured cap, often cinnamon to pale snuff-brown, without a whitish margin; network on the stem usually extends onto the base. Common under beech and oak. *B. pinicola* **, is also very similar but has a dark purplish brown cap and a wine-coloured stem with pale blood red tints on the network and the flesh tinged wine-red; occurs under pines.

Amongst numerous other species of *Boletus, B. piperatus* deserves a mention since it is unique in having a peppery taste. The cap is 3—8cm across and cinnamon-brown; stem the same colour, slender, 4—7cm × 0·5—2cm, bright yellow at the base. The pores are rust-brown, large and angular. Occurs in woods and on heaths in autumn; frequent. *B. satanas*, the Devil's Boletus †, is the only poisonous species and is recognized by the whitish cap, blood red pores and the stem with a red network of veins at the apex. It is uncommon and occurs under broad-leaved trees on limy soils.

Tylopilus (Boletus) felleus Bitter Boletus or Sponge-cap. Recognized by the dirty pink pores and brownish pink spores. Cap 6—12cm across, sienna, tawny, snuff brown, ochre or honey coloured; stem similarly coloured, ornamented with a tawny or snuff- to cigar-brown network. Taste bitter. Inedible. Occurs under beech or oak; August to November; occasional.

Suillus Distinguished from *Boletus* by the cap being distinctly to strongly sticky, slimy or glutinous when wet. Stem sometimes with the top granular-dotted, also sometimes with a ring.

Suillus (Boletus) bovinus *. Cap 5—10cm across, convex, later flattened convex and often lumpy, cinnamon or ochre buff, slimy when wet; margin paler or whitish. Stem 4—6cm × 5—8mm, yellowish to pale brown, more or less cylindrical. Tubes slightly decurrent; pores large, each containing several smaller ones, honey coloured then rusty. Flesh yellowish, reddish in stem, not or hardly turning blue. Occurs under conifers and especially pines; July to November; very common. *S. variegatus* is very similar but the cap has small, flat, fibrous scales.

Suillus (Boletus) grevillei (*B. elegans*) Larch Boletus or Sponge-cap *. Cap 3—10cm across, golden yellow, convex, later flattening or lumpy, very slimy. Stem 5—7cm × 15—20mm, cylindrical, granular or with a network and chrome- or lemon-yellow, later rusty, above a pale yellow to whitish, membranous ring, becoming rusty below. Tubes slightly to moderately decurrent. Pores small and angular, sulphur-yellow, later tinged brownish. Flesh pale yellow and deeper coloured in the stem. Always occurs under larches; March to November; common. *S. luteus* ** differs in having a dull reddish to chocolate-brown cap, and a large, purplish brown ring, below which the stem is whitish or brownish. Occurs under conifers; August to November; fairly common. *S. granulatus* * is almost a paler, ringless, less frequent version of this species.

Boletus edulis

Tylopilus felleus

Suillus bovinus

Suillus grevillei

Leccinum Differs from other boletes in that the stem is rough or woolly with small, dark-coloured to black, scurfy scales. The spore powder is ochre to snuff-brown without any olive tint.

Leccinum (**Boletus**) **variicolor** (*B. oxydabile*) Cap 5—9cm across, convex, mouse-grey with sepia, brownish grey, hazel or ochre mottling or stippling, distinctly fibrillose at first, becoming smooth, sticky in wet weather. Tubes white, tinged cream. Pores small, white or cream, bruising pale wine-coloured to rose. Stem 12·5—18cm × 2—2·5cm, white, rough with small, white to smoke-grey scales which are joined to form a network towards the base, bruising greenish yellow and intensely green to bluish green in the lower portion. Flesh reddening, becoming intense bluish green in the stem base. Occurs under birches; July to November; common. Until recently treated as a form of *L. scabrum* (*Boletus scaber*), the Brown Birch-boletus, which occurs in similar places and differs in the less grey brown cap which lacks stippling. The pores bruise ochre or cinnamon and not pinkish. The flesh remains white or merely becomes faintly tinged pinkish with no blue-green in the stem base. There are several other rather similar species.

Leccinum (**Boletus**) **versipelle** (*B. testaceoscabrum*) Orange birch-boletus or Sponge-cap **. Cap 5—15cm across, brick-red to tawny orange, hemi-spherical, slightly downy; margin extending beyond the pores as a very narrow membrane. Stem 8—15cm × 2—3cm, whitish or greyish, rough with blackish to cigar-brown scales, swollen towards the base. Pores small, round, pale greyish, finally pale dirty grey-brown, bruising a dull wine-colour. Flesh whitish then greyish mauve or slate, finally slaty black, bluish green at stem base. Occurs under birches, July to November; frequent.

Agarics or gill fungi

Fruit-bodies with soft, easily decaying flesh; sometimes tougher and after drying, reviving on wetting, but never woody. Spore-bearing surface on gills. Stem usually central but sometimes absent or lateral; the latter are dealt with first and are followed by the milk-caps (*Lactarius*), the brittle-gills (*Russula*) and the wax-gills (*Hygrophorus*). The rest of the agarics follow in groups arranged according to spore colour.

Stemless or laterally-stemmed gill fungi

Schizophyllum commune Split-gill. Cap 1—4cm across, greyish to greyish fawn, whitish when dry, fan- or kidney-shaped, often lobed, thickly hairy, stemless or with a stem-like base; margin incurved. Gills grey-brown to purplish, narrow; when dry, the edges splitting lengthwise and rolling outwards and round, covering the space between the gills. Flesh thin and tough. Occurs on dead wood of broad-leaved trees, especially stacked timber throughout the year. Common in mainland Europe especially in the south, uncommon in Britain except the south-east.

Panellus (**Panus**) **stipticus** Styptic Fungus. Cap 1—3cm across, pale cinnamon-brown to pale dull yellowish brown, flattish convex, thin, more or less kidney-shaped, scurfy; margin incurved. Gills yellowish or pale cinnamon, very narrow, closely spaced and connected by veins. Stem short, 5—20mm × 2—3mm, whitish, widening into the cap and attached to one side of it. Spores white. Flesh toughish; taste bitter and astringent. Fruit-bodies crowded together, often in tiers. Occurs on dead stumps and branches; throughout the year; common.

Leccinum variicolor

Leccinum versipelle

Schizophyllum commune

Panellus stipticus

Crepidotus mollis Soft Slipper Toadstool. Cap 3—7cm across, yellowish cream-coloured to whitish, kidney- to shell-shaped, flat or wavy, smooth, often in tiers, with a narrow or rudimentary stem-like attachment. Gills pale, later dull cinnamon. Differs from other species of *Crepidotus* by having a gelatinous layer in the flesh which, if the cap is gently pulled apart laterally, may be seen connecting the separated portions. Spore deposit yellow-brown. Occurs on dead branches and stumps of broad-leaved trees; July to November; fairly common.

Pleurotus ostreatus Oyster Mushroom **. Cap 7—13cm across, shell-shaped to rounded flap-shaped, convex, later flattening; deep bluish grey in colour to almost black when young, becoming smoky brown or pale yellowish brown to umber. Usually many clustered together, with a narrow point of attachment or with a short, thick, white stem, 2—3cm×1—2cm attached towards or at one side, with a woolly base. Gills white, becoming pale yellowish, deeply decurrent and anastomosing at the base. Flesh white and a little fibrous. Spore deposit lilac in the mass. Occurs on trunks, stumps, etc., usually of broad-leaved trees, especially beech; throughout the year; common.

Lactarius Milk-caps

A large genus of agarics easily recognized by the white, coloured, or rarely, watery fluid produced on wounding. The flesh breaks easily and the spores are amyloid (i.e. turn blackish violet with iodine solutions). They are closely related to the russulas or brittle-gills but mostly lack the bright colours frequent in that genus. The gills are usually decurrent, whilst in the russulas they are rarely so.

Lactarius piperatus Peppery Milk-cap. Entirely white. Cap 5—22cm across, tinged creamy, shallow funnel-shaped to umbilicate with convex and, initially, inrolled margin. Gills white then creamy, decurrent, crowded, narrow and forking. Stem 3—7cm×2—5cm, cylindrical or widening upwards. Milk white with a very acrid, burning taste. Occurs in broad-leaved woods; July to October; frequent. *L. vellereus*, the Fleecy Milk-cap, is very similar, but is larger with the cap 10—30cm across and more saucer-shaped. It may be recognized by the velvety cap and the widely spaced gills. Occurs in broad-leaved woods; August to December; common. *L. controversus* * is also white and resembles *L. piperatus* but the cap sometimes becomes blotched with pale lilac or carmine. The stem is shorter and the gills are pale rosy buff. Occurs under poplars inland and with *Salix repens* in sand-dune slacks; September to November; uncommon.

Lactarius torminosus Woolly Milk-cap†. Cap 4—12cm across, pale salmony flesh-coloured or salmon-buff to pale strawberry-pink, convex, later with a central depression; also somewhat indistinctly concentrically banded, margin incurved and shaggy with hairs. Gills pale flesh colour to pale salmon, thin, narrow and slightly decurrent. Stem 6—9cm×1·5—2·5cm, cylindrical and delicately downy, pale flesh-coloured to pale salmon. Milk white, hot and acrid tasting. Occurrs on the ground in woods and on heaths; August to September; frequent. *L. pubescens* is very similar but smaller and paler coloured. Occurs under birches on sandy soil; occasional.

Crepidotus mollis

*Pleurotus
ostreatus*

Lactarius piperatus

*Lactarius
torminosus*

Lactarius deliciosus Saffron Milk-cap**. Cap 3—10cm across, orange-red with concentric darker bands, convex and umbilicate, later shallow funnel-shaped, becoming tinged greenish in places, slightly sticky. Gills slightly decurrent, pale orange-yellow to orange-ochre or saffron coloured, broad and closely spaced. Stem 3—4cm×1·5—2cm orange to brick-coloured, more or less cylindrical, rigid, solid, later becoming hollow, becoming tinged green in places. Milk carrot-coloured, unchanging, later slowly fading; taste mild or slightly bitter. Occurs under pines and sometimes spruce; July to October; common in eastern Europe, becoming less frequent westwards, rare in Britain. This description applies to *L. deliciosus* in the narrow sense; a number of closely similar species have been distinguished in recent years within the old, broad concept of this species. In Britain and western Europe, *L. deterrimus* seems to be the commonest. It is recognized by the milk becoming purplish in ten minutes and turning dark dull wine-red in about thirty minutes after exposure. Also recognized by the bitter taste of the milk and by the cylindrical stem. The cap colour is less reddish and the whole fungus is very prone to turn green in places. It is mainly found under spruce but also under pines and is less good to eat than *L. deliciosus. L. semisanguifluus* is similar but the milk begins to darken in three minutes and the stem widens upwards; it is found under pines. *L. subsalmoneus* (*L. salmonicolor*) has a bright orange-yellow or apricot cap and does not or hardly becomes blotched green. The milk of the reddish tawny-capped *L. sanguifluus* is blood-red from the start. *L. chrysorrheus* is a noteworthy species easily recognized by its milk turning sulphur-yellow a minute or so after exposure to the air. The cap is yellowish flesh-coloured and concentrically banded. Occurs under oaks; occasional.

Lactarius blennius Slimy Milk-cap. Cap 4—11cm across, flattish convex, later with a depression, palish olive to greenish grey or pale greyish sepia with darker, drop-like markings often concentrically arranged, very slimy when wet; margin incurved. Gills white to very pale buff, brownish-greyish where wounded, slightly decurrent, narrow. Stem 4—5cm×10—15mm, pale olive or pale grey, cylindrical, slimy. Milk white, drying grey; taste very hot and acrid. Occurs in broad-leaved woods especially beech; August to November; very common.

Lactarius turpis (*L. necator L. plumbeus*) Ugly Milk-cap. Cap 6—30cm, dark olive-brown, umber or olive blackish, margin slightly paler, convex, later with a depression. Gills cream to yellowish buff, becoming pale sepia where wounded. Stem 4—8cm×10—25mm, short and stout, colour the same as the cap or whitish, slimy, often pitted, hollow. Milk white, very hot and acrid. Occurs under birches, especially where damp; August to November; common. All parts turn purple-violet with ammonia or caustic alkali solutions.

Lactarius pyrogalus Cap 5—10cm across, dingy greyish fawn, sometimes with yellowish tinge, faintly concentrically banded, flat, later very broadly funnel-shaped, slightly sticky but not slimy in wet weather. Gills yellowish to flesh-coloured then cinnamon-ochre, slightly decurrent. Stem 4—6cm×12mm, the same colour as the cap but paler. Milk white, very hot and acrid; a drop with caustic alkali solution on a sheet of glass turns orange-yellow. Occurs under hazels; September to November; fairly common. *L. circellatus* differs in having a strongly banded cap and yellowish gills, also the milk does not react with alkali. Occurs under hornbeams, uncommon.

*Lactarius
deliciosus*

Lactarius blennius

Lactarius turpis

*Lactarius
pyrogalus*

Lactarius glyciosmus Coconut-scented Milk-cap *. Cap 2—7cm across, usually greyish lilac, sometimes dull buff, convex, later with a depression, sometimes with a small point in the centre. Gills pale yellowish to pale flesh then greyish lilac, narrow, decurrent. Stem 2·5—5cm × 4—8mm, coloured as cap but paler or yellowish, cylindrical, downy. Milk white; taste mild at first then becoming a little hot and acrid. Odour suggests coconuts by which it is recognized. Occurs on wettish ground in woods; August to November; common. *L. vietus*, the Grey Milk-cap, is rather similar in colour but lacks the odour of coconuts and the milk becomes grey on drying, often producing a grey spotting of the gills. Occurs frequently under birches, especially in damp places; fairly common.

Lactarius rufus Rufous Milk-cap. Cap 5—10cm across, red-brown, bay or dark brick, convex, later flattened, finally with a central depression, usually with the centre raised or with a point. Gills yellowish at first, later like the cap but paler, somewhat decurrent. Stem 5—8cm × 1cm, coloured as the cap but paler, cylindrical, becoming hollow. Milk white, after about a minute tastes very hot and acrid, so take care to taste only a small amount and allow time for it to take effect! Occurs in pine woods; June to November; very common.

Lactarius quietus Oak Milk-cap. Cap 3—9cm across, dull reddish brown with cinnamon tints, often with vague darker concentric banding or spotting, convex, later flattened or with a shallow depression. Gills brownish white, later pale reddish brown with a slight mauvy bloom, slightly decurrent. Stem 4—9cm × 1—1·5cm, coloured as the cap or darker, more or less cylindrical, often furrowed lengthwise. Milk white or slightly creamy; taste mild or slightly bitterish. Odour slightly oily or suggestive of bugs. Occurs on the ground always near oaks; September to November; very common.

Lactarius mitissimus Cap 3—8cm across, bright, slightly brownish orange or apricot, convex, later flattened, velvety to the touch, slightly sticky; margin incurved. Gills palish ochre, adnate to slightly decurrent. Stem 2·5—8cm × 8—12mm, same colour as the cap, cylindrical. Milk abundant, white; taste mild. Occurs on the ground in both coniferous and broad-leaved woods; September to November; frequent. *L. aurantiacus* is very similar but the milk tastes slowly hot; it is not found in Britain. *L. fulvissimus* (*L. ichoratus* of Neuhoff) is another orangy species but has browner and darker tones and may be brown in the centre. The cap surface is not velvety to the touch and is often puckered, whilst the milk is slightly hot and turns pale yellow on a white handkerchief. *L. rubrocinctus* closely resembles it and occurs in the same places. It is rather paler and duller in colour, also the milk does not turn yellowish on a handkerchief. There is usually, but not always, a reddish band at the top of the stem where the gills join it; the young gills have a dull violet tinge. *L. volemus* **, again is orange but has a fishy odour and the gills bruise brown.

L. helvus †, has a dull yellowish cap with small, flat scales. It is easily recognized by the 'milk' being like water and the strong odour of curry it produces when dried. Occurs in coniferous woods on heaths and moors. Although mildly poisonous, it is sometimes used in a powdered form as a condiment.

Lactarius
glyciosmus

Lactarius rufus

Lactarius quietus

Lactarius
mitissimus

Lactarius hepaticus (*L. theiogalus* of some authors). Cap 2·5—7cm across, liver-coloured to chestnut, convex, later flattened, sometimes with a central pimple; margin often crimped or crisped with tiny lobes. Gills pale buff, later deep buff to pale ochre with a mauvy bloom, slightly decurrent. Stem 3—4cm× 5—10mm, reddish brown to dark brick-coloured, cylindrical. Milk white, drying yellowish (a drop on a white handkerchief turns sulphur-yellow in a minute or two). Common under pines in southern Britain and Europe, rarer northwards; September to November.

Lactarius tabidus (*L. theiogalus* of some authors). Cap 2—4cm across, dull ochre-buff to yellowish rusty or dull orange-ochre, shallow convex with a central depression, often with a pimple in the middle. Gills pale yellowish cinnamon with a rosy tint, slightly decurrent. Milk white, rather scanty, a drop turns yellow slowly on a white handkerchief and goes orange if caustic alkali is added; taste slightly burning and acrid, almost mild. Occurs under broad-leaved trees especially birch; August to November; common.

Lactarius subdulcis Cap 5—8cm across, red-brown, rusty or dark cinnamon, paling to buff, often darker in the centre, convex, later with a depression, smooth and dry. Gills for a while whitish then rosy buff with a wine-coloured glint, adnate to slightly decurrent. Stem 2·5—5cm×4—10mm, the same colour as the cap but paler above, cylindrical, sometimes furrowed lengthwise. Milk plentiful and white, does *not* turn yellow on a handkerchief (compare the last two species); taste mild then slightly bitter but not hot. Occurs in broad-leaved woods, especially beech; August to November; common. Recognized amongst the red-brown species by the taste of the milk. *L. camphoratus*, the Curry-scented Milk-cap, is another red-brown species and is recognized by the dark red-brown stem which is darker than the cap, the watery milk with only a few white curds and the smell of curry when dried. *L. cimicarius* also has watery milk and an odour of curry when dried but the cap is dark bay brown and has a strong odour of bugs when fresh.

Russula Brittle-gills

A large genus of some 190 European species easily recognized by their brittle flesh and, with very few exceptions, brittle gills that break into fragments when lightly rubbed. The caps are usually brightly coloured: yellow, red, purple, violet tinted or green. In common with some other genera they form a mutually advantageous partnership called 'mycorrhiza' with the roots of forest trees. Many of the commoner species are fairly easy to recognize, but others require microscopic examination to name them correctly. The colour of the spores when scraped into a thick layer and the taste of the gill and cap flesh are important for identification. The spores are amyloid.

Russula delica Milk-white Russula*. Cap 5—18cm across, whitish, often tinged yellow brownish, convex, cup- or funnel-shaped, matt; margin strongly inrolled. Gills whitish, often tinged bluish towards the stem, decurrent. Stem 2—6cm×2—5cm, white, often bluish at apex. Flesh white, unchanging. Spores white. Taste hot and acrid with a bitter tang. Odour distinctive, slightly of bugs, sometimes fishy. Occurs under both broad-leaved and coniferous trees; September to November; common. Several varieties have been described, some as distinct species. Somewhat similar in appearance to *Lactarius piperatus* and *L. vellereus* but lacks the milk.

*Lactarius
hepaticus*

Lactarius tabidus

*Lactarius
subdulcis*

Russula delica

Russula nigricans Blackening Russula (or Brittle-gill) *. Cap 10–20cm across, dirty white becoming brown and finally black, developing a deep depression, dry; margin incurved at first. Gills straw to olive, greyish rose on bruising, eventually turning black, adnate, very thick and widely spaced. Stem 3–8cm × 1–4cm, at first white then dull brown and finally black, hard. Flesh white becoming greyish rose on exposure to air and finally grey to black. Spores white. Taste slowly hot. Odour fruity. Occurs under both broad-leaved and coniferous trees; August to November; very common.

Russula densifolia (*R. acrifolia* of Romagnesi) *. Usually smaller than the last: cap 5–15cm across, whitish or dull brown in centre or all over, eventually blackish, flattened convex at first, later with a depression, champagne-glass shaped or widely funnel-shaped, sticky when moist; margin incurved at first. Gills white to pale cream, slightly decurrent, closely spaced (compare the last species) rather narrow and not thick. Stem 3–6cm × 1–3cm, white then dull brown to blackish, reddish on bruising, hard. Flesh white, reddening, very soon greying as well, finally dark grey to brownish blackish. Spores white. Taste hot or very hot, but sometimes almost mild. Odour not distinctive. Occurs under both broad-leaved and coniferous trees; fairly common. Probably often mistaken for the uncommon *R. adusta* whose flesh does not redden or only very slightly and goes grey after thirty minutes but not blackish. Its taste is mild, it smells of old wine casks and it grows under conifers. *Russula albonigra* (*R. anthracina* of Romagnesi), the Black and White Russula, is similar but is, at first, completely white and blackens rapidly wherever it is bruised, giving it a black-and-white or pepper-and-salt appearance. Occurs under both broad-leaved and coniferous trees; uncommon.

Russula sororia (*R. amoenolens* of Romagnesi). Cap 3–6cm across, sepia, often greyish, sometimes white, slightly sticky when moist; margin closely furrowed and has small warts. Gills creamy to dirty whitish, edge browning, straight or arched. Stem 3–6cm × 1–2cm, whitish. Taste unpleasant, oily and slowly very hot. Odour rancid or suggesting Camembert cheese. Occurs under oaks; September to November; frequent. Romagnesi's *R. sororia* is larger and the spore shape (under the microscope) is rounder.

Russula foetens Foetid Russula (or Brittle-gill). Cap 5–15cm across, dull brownish ochre to honey-coloured; globose at first, later convex, thick and fleshy; surface slimy or glutinous; margin furrowed and warted. Gills creamy, often brown-spotted, thickish and well-spaced. Stem 5–12cm × 1·5–4cm, whitish to buff, cylindrical or swollen in the middle, containing irregular cavities, hard and rigid but easily breaking. Flesh whitish. Taste of gills very hot but that of stem centre sometimes almost mild; in addition bitter or oily. Odour strongly oily or rancid. Occurs under broad-leaved or coniferous trees; August to November; common. *R. laurocerasi* is very similar and is recognized by its odour of bitter almonds.

Russula nigricans

Russula densifolia

Russula sororia

Russula foetens

Russula ochroleuca Common Yellow Russula (or Brittle-gill) *. Cap 4—12cm across, ochre, yellow or sometimes yellowish green; margin smooth, later furrowed. Gills creamy. Stem 4—7cm×1·5—2·5cm, somewhat fragile, white, greying with age especially when water-logged. Taste from mild to moderately hot. Spores whitish to cream. Occurs under broad-leaved and coniferous trees; August to November, mainly October; very common, the commonest of the russulas and one of the commonest of all agarics.

Russula claroflava Yellow Swamp Russula **. Cap 4—10cm across, yellow to ochre-yellow, convex; margin smooth at first, later slightly furrowed. Gills palish ochre. Stem 4—10cm×1—2cm, soft but not fragile. All parts turning dark grey to black on bruising, or with age. Taste mild or slightly hot when young. Spores ochre. Occurs under birches especially on wet ground; September to November; frequent; occasionally May to June also. *R. lutea* * is another yellow-capped but smaller species being 2—7cm across. Recognized by the deep saffron coloured gills and the fruity odour suggesting apricots. The taste is mild and the cap is sometimes apricot or tinted with coral or may be entirely coral coloured. Occurs under broad-leaved trees; July to November; fairly frequent.

Russula fellea Geranium-scented Russula or Bitter Brittle-gill. Cap 4—9cm across, straw-coloured to pale ochre-honey or buff; margin smooth or slightly furrowed. Gills the same colour as the cap but slightly paler. Stem 2—6cm× 1—2cm, the same colour as the gills. Spores white. Taste very hot and bitter. Recognized by the odour of cultivated 'geraniums' (*Pelargonium zonale*). Stem when rubbed with a crystal of iron alum, turns cream, not salmon as in most russulas. Occurs under beech; August to November; common.

Russula cyanoxantha The Charcoal Burner (from the French 'Charbonnier'). Cap 5—15cm across, sometimes one colour but usually a mixture of colours, such as dullish lilac, purplish, wine-coloured, olive, greenish or brownish, sometimes entirely green (var. *pelteraui*), at first globose, later flattening, firm to hard, greasy when moist, with faint, branching veins radiating from the centre. Gills whitish or very pale cream and rather narrow, at times forked, flexible (*not* brittle), oily to the touch. Stem 5—10cm×1·5—3cm, white but sometimes flushed purple, hard, giving no, or a slightly greenish, reaction when rubbed with iron alum, *not* salmon as with most russulas. Spores whitish. Occurs under broad-leaved trees; July to November; very common. *Russula grisea* ** (in the broad sense), is rather similar but the gills and spores are creamy and the stem turns salmon when rubbed with iron alum. It may prove to be a complex of several, closely similar species. One of these, which is probably distinct, is *R. parazurea* ** whose cap is usually greyish or bluish grey or may be other dullish colours, sometimes with greenish, brownish, wine-coloured or violet tints. Occurs under broad-leaved trees; frequent.

*Russula
ochroleuca*

Russula claroflava

Russula fellea

*Russula
cyanoxantha*

Russula vesca Bare-toothed Russula (or Brittle-gill) **. Cap 6—10cm across,
very variable in colour, often with pastel tints, from dark or pale wine-coloured
to buff, sometimes with olive or greenish tints or even whitish, somewhat
globose at first, later flattened convex, firm and smooth, the skin tending to
retreat from the cap margin leaving the underlying flesh visible. Gills whitish to
very pale cream, rather closely spaced. Stem 3—10cm × 1·5—2·5cm, white, firm
and rather hard. Spores whitish. Taste nutty. Both the stem and gills react
exceptionally vigorously to rubbing with iron alum and turn deep salmon pink.
Occurs under broad-leaved trees, June to October; common.

Russula xerampelina (in part *R. faginea* of Romagnesi) **. Cap 5—14cm across,
very varied in colour: dull purple, dull purplish red, blood-coloured, wine-
coloured, cinnamon, honey, buff, straw, fawn, brick or dull dark brown or
various combinations of these colours, moderately firm but sometimes hard, dry
and matt; margin smooth, furrowed with age. Gills pale to medium ochre, fairly
broad and thick. Stem 3—11cm × 1—3cm, white or tinted rose, staining honey to
brownish ochre especially on bruising and along the faint veining, firm or even
hard at times, reacting dark green when rubbed with iron alum. Spores medium
ochre. Taste mild. Odour crab-like, especially with age. Occurs under broad-
leaved trees especially beech and oak; August to November; frequent.
Recognized by the brown staining of the stem, the crab odour and the green
iron reaction. All these characteristics it shares with *R. erythropus*, but the cap
and stem of this are usually pale to dark blood-coloured or red, but occasionally
white and it occurs under conifers. No other russulas have the green iron
reaction. *R. xerampelina* is divided by Romagnesi and others into several
closely related species and varieties according to cap coloration, spore
ornamentation, etc.

Russula sardonia (*R. drimeia*). Cap 4—10cm across, violet or purplish or
brownish red, greenish or ochre to yellowish, hard. Gills at first primrose then
yellowish ochre. Stem 3—8cm × 1—1·5cm, sometimes white but usually entirely
pale lilac to greyish rose, firm; surface as if powdered. Spores palish ochre.
Flesh pale straw-coloured. Taste very hot. Odour slightly fruity. Concentrated
ammonia turns gills and flesh slowly rose and this, combined with the hot taste,
distinguishes the species. Occurs under pines; August to November; frequent.

Russula atropurpurea Blackish-purple Russla *. Cap 4—10cm across,
typically deep purplish red with darker centre, but sometimes with more violet
or more reddish tints, often with yellowish or brownish creamy areas; margin
smooth except when old. Gills palish cream. Stem 3—5cm × 1—2cm, white, often
becoming greyish with age, fairly firm at first, later softer and easily broken.
Taste from almost mild to moderately hot. Odour slightly fruity. Under broad-
leaved or coniferous trees; July to November; common. Easily recognized by
the cap colour in typical specimens; also by the combination of creamy gills
with whitish spores.

Russula vesca

Russula xerampelina

Russula sardonia

Russula atropurpurea

Russula fragilis Fragile Russula (or Brittle-gill). Cap 2—6cm across, very variable in colour, usually purplish- or violet-tinted and rather pale, but also purplish red, purple-violet, olive-greenish or even lemon-yellow, often with combinations of these colours, with darker, paler or olive-tinted centre, usually small, delicate and fragile. Gills white to very pale cream, their margins having tiny nicks along them. Stem 2·5—6cm×0·5—1·5cm, white, more or less cylindrical to slightly club-shaped. Spores whitish. Taste very hot. Odour slightly fruity. Occurs under broad-leaved or coniferous trees; August to November; common. *R. betularum* (*R. emetica* var. *betularum*) is rather similar but has a deep to pale rose cap, often with a yellowish buff centre and the stem is longer than the cap diameter. Occurs under birches; common.

Russula emetica (*R. emetica* var. *longipes* according to Romagnesi) The Sickener or Emetic Russula†. Cap 5—10cm across, scarlet, cherry- or blood-red, sometimes with ochre-tinted to white areas, shiny, sticky when moist; margin often furrowed with age; skin peeling easily to reveal pink to red flesh beneath, but deeper flesh is white. Gills cream then pale straw. Stem 5—8cm× 1—2cm, cylindrical or more usually somewhat swollen towards the base, fragile. Spores whitish. Taste very hot. Odour slightly fruity. Occurs under conifers especially pines; August to November; common. Recognized by the bright coloured, fragile cap and long, often narrow club-shaped stem. *R. emetica* var. *silvestris* is similar but less brilliantly coloured and has a shorter, cylindrical stem. It favours mossy cushions in oak woods but may also occur under conifers.

Russula mairei Beechwood Sickener. Cap 3—6cm across, red or pink to entirely white, typically rather firm or thick fleshed, convex to flattened convex. Gills white with greenish tinge then cream. Stem 2·5—4·5cm×1—1·5cm, white, cylindrical, rather hard. Spores whitish. Taste very hot; odour faintly of coconut when young. Occurs under beeches; August to November; quite common. Formerly confused with *R. emetica* and its var. *silvestris*, but quite distinct and recognized by the paler colour, more squat and firm build and certain microscopic and chemical differences.

Hygrophorus Wax-gills

Recognized by the waxy appearance, especially of the gills, which are narrow wedge-shaped in cross-section instead of almost parallel sided as in most other agarics. Many species are bright coloured: red, orange or yellow, but some are white, buff or shades of brown. Spores white. The genus is now often subdivided into three, *Hygrophorus*, *Camarophyllus* and *Hygrocybe* on anatomical grounds.

Hygrophorus chrysaspis Ivory Slime Cap. Cap 3—10cm across, white with centre eventually cream, convex, later flat, slimy; margin inrolled. Gills white to cream, shortly decurrent, thick and well-spaced. Stem 4—10cm×6 × 10mm, white, slimy, with white dots and often globules of water at apex. Whole fungus blotched with russet or rust with age. The base of the stem turns brownish-orangy-chrome-yellow with caustic alkali solutions. Occurs under beeches; August to November; common. Often confused with the very similar *H. eburneus* which does not become brown-blotched with age, nor does it give the colour reaction with alkali. It is less common and is found under oaks rather than beeches.

Russula fragilis

Russula emetica

Russula mairei

Hygrophorus chrysaspis

Hygrophorus hypothejus Cap 2—6cm across, olive-brown at first then paling, somewhat streaky, convex, later flattened or with a depression, slimy. Gills pale yellow, decurrent, well-spaced and thick. Stem 5—10cm × 4—10mm, white to yellowish, tapering downwards, slimy on lower portion below a ring-like termination near the top. Flesh white to yellowish. Occurs under pines; October to November, resistant to frost; common.

Hygrophorus (Camarophyllus) pratensis Buff Meadow Cap (or Wax-gill) **. Cap 2·5—8cm across, dull pale tawny or buff, convex, later flattened, often with a central raised area. Gills pale buff, deeply decurrent, thick and very widely spaced, often connected at their bases by veins. Stem 4—6cm × 1—1·5cm, coloured as the cap but paler, gradually widening upwards into the cap. Flesh buff. Occurs in grassland; August to December; frequent. *H. nemoreus* * is very similar but more slender, has small fibres in the cap surface, a mealy odour and the stem is powdery at the apex. Occurs in woods.

Hygrophorus (Hygrocybe) psittacinus Parrot Toadstool. Cap 2—5cm across, green at first due to the slime that covers it, later yellowish, whitish or brick-coloured and finally purplish, bell-shaped at first then flatter and umbonate; margin radially striate. Gills yellow, greenish at the base, broad, thick and moderately spaced. Stem 4—7cm × 4—7mm, green at first from the slime and remaining so at the apex but elsewhere becoming yellow, cylindrical. Occurs in grassland and on lawns; July to November; frequent.

Hygrophorus (Hygrocybe) nigrescens Blackening Meadow Cap (or Wax-gill). Cap 1—5cm across, lemon-yellow, orange or scarlet, soon blackening, bell-shaped or bluntly conical, often somewhat irregular and lobed. Gills white, tinged yellowish green towards the base, adnexed, finally free, very broad, thick and widely spaced. Stem 5—7cm × 1—2cm, lemon-yellow or tinged with scarlet but soon streaked with black, white at the base, easily splitting lengthwise and hollow. Occurs on lawns and in grassy places; July to November; frequent. *H. conicus* is very similar but has a sharper pointed cap and lacks the white base to the stem. *H. coccineus,* the Scarlet Hood *, is also somewhat similar but the cap is more bell-shaped and rounded on top. It is bright scarlet and does not blacken, whilst the gills are between adnate and slightly decurrent. It also occurs in grassy places. *H. puniceus* *, another grassland species, is also scarlet or blood-red and may be recognized by its large size, the cap being 4—8cm or even up to 10cm across. It is campanulate, but rather irregular and often lop-sided in shape.

There are a number of orange to yellow species of *Hygrophorus* but they are often difficult to identify without microscopic examination of the spores.

H. calyptraeformis, the Pink Meadow Cap, is easily recognized since it is the only species that is pink with a slight mauvy tinge. It is tall, 6—12cm high and has a conical cap. It grows in grassland in autumn; uncommon.

Hygrophorus
hypothejus

Hygrophorus
pratensis

Hygrophorus
psittacinus

Hygrophorus
nigrescens

White or pale spored agarics, excluding *Lactarius, Russula* and *Hygrophorus*   Key to genera:

1a   Stem with a ring or volva
    2a   Stem base with a volva, or bulbous with a rim, or with woolly scales;
        flat moveable scales on cap   *Amanita* page 66
    2b   Stem base without volva or rim; scales on cap if present, not
        moveable.
        3a   Gills free   *Lepiota* page 70
        3b ↓ Gills adnexed   *Cystoderma* page 70, *Oudemansiella* page 72
        3c   Gills decurrent   *Armillaria* page 72
1b   Stem without a ring or volva   see page 72

Amanita Recognized by possessing a volva or a bulbous stem with a rim of woolly scales on the bulb, and by having scales on the cap that may be moved if pushed with the finger nail. Gills usually free and there is often a ring on stem.

Amanita phalloides The Death Cap †† . Cap 7—10cm, greenish or yellowish olive, but sometimes paling to almost white, streaked with radiating fibres within the surface, somewhat slimy when moist, sometimes with flat, white, skin-like patches of the veil; the skin of the cap may be easily peeled as in the edible mushroom! Gills white, free and rather closely spaced. Stem 8—12cm× 1·5—2cm, white or coloured like the cap but paler, smooth, or the surface cracking into very thin, fringed patches, solid at first then hollow, narrowing upwards, with a prominent skirt-like ring near the top. The base of the stem is bulbous and enclosed in a goblet-shaped, white, skinny bag (the volva). See fig. 4 for a diagram of the fruit-body structure. Odour when old sickly or foetid. Occurs under broad-leaved trees especially beech and oak; July to October; frequent. Very poisonous, a quarter of a cap being sufficient to be fatal. The symptoms which are intense abdominal pain, vomiting and diarrhoea, do not commence until six to fifteen hours after consumption. Call a doctor immediately if poisoning is suspected. *A. verna* †† is very similar and differs mainly by being entirely white.

Amanita virosa Destroying Angel †† . Very similar to *A. phalloides* and differing mainly by having a shaggy stem as well as by being entirely white. Occurs under broad-leaved trees; August to October; uncommon.

Amanita caesarea ** The 'Orange' of the French, the 'Egg Fungus' of the Italians and the 'Boletus' of ancient Rome: a highly esteemed, edible species. Cap 8—20cm across, orange or sometimes yellow, smooth and without scales. Gills yellow, free. Stem 6—14cm×1—2·5cm, yellow or orange with a skirt-like yellow ring near the top and a skinny, bag-like, white volva at the base. Occurs in poor, acid woodlands in southern Germany, Austria, southern France and southern Europe, absent from Britain.

Amanita muscaria Fly Agaric †† . Cap 10—20cm across, scarlet or orange, sometimes fading to yellow, rounded at first, later expanding to convex, finally flattening, covered at first with white, flattish to thick warts, usually abundant but at times disappearing, slimy when moist; margin slightly striate. Gills white, free and closely spaced. Stem 10—22cm×2·5cm, white, solid but later hollow, striate above the white, skirt-like ring situated near the top; base bulbous, with concentric rings of white, woolly scales. Occurs under birches and pines; August to November; fairly common. The name comes from its use as a fly poison. Also called the 'Sacred Mushroom' as it was used to produce hallucinations in religious practices. However, it is dangerously poisonous.

Amanita
phalloides

left
Amanita virosa
right
Amanita caesarea

Amanita muscaria

Amanita pantherina The Panther ††. Cap 6—10cm across, olive-umber, smoky brown or greyish olive, convex, later flattening, covered with numerous, small, white warts, sticky when moist; margin striate. Gills white and free. Stem 7—9cm×1cm, white, cylindrical, with a somewhat narrow, not flaring ring half-way down, smooth on its upper surface, often obliquely attached and tending to disappear; base of stem bulbous with several, concentric, narrow, membranous rings. Spores not blackening with iodine solutions. Occurs under broad-leaved trees, especially beech; August to October; uncommon.

Amanita excelsa (A. spissa) *. Cap 6—12cm across, greyish or umber-brown, convex and covered with greyish, flattened warts which eventually disappear; margin not striate. Gills white, slightly decurrent and closely spaced. Stem 8—15cm×2—4cm, white, striate above the skirt-like ring, which is striate above and attached to the upper half; base swollen and covered with concentrically arranged, woolly scales. Spores amyloid, i.e. blackish with iodine solutions. Occurs under coniferous and broad-leaved trees; June to October; fairly common. Resembles the last species with which it is often confused, but the ring which is striate above and on the upper half of the stem, the greyish warts, the non-striate cap margin, the stem base without narrow rings and the amyloid spores distinguish it.

Amanita rubescens The Blusher **. Cap 8—12cm across, reddish fawn or reddish brown, convex, flattening later, covered with scattered, dirty white, greyish or yellowish, flattish warts or patches; margin slightly striate with age. Gills white, spotted red when old, thin and soft, attached to the stem by a slight tooth. Stem 7—12cm×3—4cm, white or tinged reddish below especially if handled, striate above the white, flaring ring which is striate on the upper surface; base bulbous, with concentric woolly scales. Flesh white becoming pinkish when broken. Spores amyloid, blackening with iodine solutions. Occurs under both coniferous and broad-leaved trees; July to October; very common. Slightly poisonous when raw, but excellent cooked. Take care that all specimens, especially young ones, used for cooking show some signs of red coloration so as to be certain that they are not the very poisonous *A. pantherina*.

Amanita citrina (A. mappa) False Death Cap. Cap 6—9cm across, lemon-yellow, often rather pale, sometimes white (var. *alba*), convex, flattening later, smooth and shining when dry, with numerous, flat, white to pale dull ochre yellow warts or patches which are the remains of the veil. Gills white, adnexed, sometimes with a yellowish edge, closely spaced and narrow. Stem 5—8cm× 1—1·5cm, white, tapering upwards and striate above the membranous ring which is attached well above the middle. The ring is striate and white on the upper surface and yellowish below. Base of stem bulbous with a narrow ledge or ridge running round the upper portion of the bulb. Odour of raw potatoes when broken. Occurs under both coniferous and broad-leaved trees especially oak and beech; July to November; common. At one time thought to be poisonous but now known to be harmless though unpleasant to eat.

*Amanita
pantherina*

Amanita excelsa

Amanita rubescens

Amanita citrina

Amanita (*Amanitopsis*) *fulva* Tawny Grisette **. Cap 4—10cm, bright orangy brown to date-brown, bell-shaped, later convex with a broad, low umbo, sometimes with whitish patches of the veil; margin strongly striate. Gills white or tinged yellowish and free. Stem 7—20cm × 5—10mm, tinged tawny but paler than the cap, slightly scaly, without a ring but with a membranous, loosely sheathing, yellowish volva at the base. Occurs under broad-leaved trees especially birch on acid soils; May to November; very common. *A. vaginata*, the Grisette **, is similar but more robust and has a greyish or grey-brown cap. Occurs under broad-leaved trees especially beech; July to November; fairly common.

Lepiota Although quite a large genus many of the species are not common. It is characterized by having white spores, free gills and a ring on the stem. Scales on the cap, if present, are not moveable. The larger species, which have large, moveable rings, are sometimes placed in a separate genus, *Macrolepiota*.

Lepiota (*Macrolepiota*) *procera* Parasol Mushroom **. Cap 10—25cm across, at first oval so that the young fungus looks like a drumstick, later bell-shaped and finally convex and umbonate. The umber to greyish brown skin breaks up into large, coarse, thick scales that tend to turn upwards at their lower ends, the whitish underlying cap flesh showing between them; margin of cap fringed. Gills white, soft, closely spaced, broad, free from the stem and separated from it by a gap. Stem 15—30cm × 15—20mm, with a greyish brown felty covering that cracks into snake-skin like markings. It tapers upwards and is swollen at the base. It pulls out from the cap as if from a socket. A ring is attached well above the middle and is large and thick, white above, brown below, becoming detached so that it can be moved up and down the stem. Flesh white, does not change colour when cut. Occurs at the edges of broad-leaved woods and in clearings, also in grassy places away from woods; July to November; fairly frequent. One of the best of the edible agarics. *L. rhacodes*, the Shaggy Parasol **, is rather similar but rather more robust, has shaggier scales, a whitish stem without brown markings and the flesh turns brownish-reddish when cut. Occurs under trees and hedges in woods, parks and gardens, especially on rich soil. There are several, rather similar, smaller species.

Lepiota cristata Stinking Parasol ?†. Cap 2—7cm across, white and silky, with numerous small, reddish brown scales, densely crowded or forming a continuous layer over the centre, bell-shaped, later flattening and umbonate. Gills white, free and closely spaced. Stem 4—6cm × 3—8mm, white, yellowish or tinged red-brown, cylindrical, fragile, with a narrow, white ring in the middle. Odour unpleasant when crushed, with a suggestion of radish. Occurs in grassy places, by paths and under hedges; August to November; fairly common.

Cystoderma (*Lepiota*) *amianthinum* Saffron Parasol. Cap 3—5cm across, pale ochre-yellow, bell-shaped, later convex to flat, often radially wrinkled, at first, covered with mealy granules later often smooth; margin minutely toothed. Gills creamy, adnate and closely spaced. Stem 3—5cm × 4—6mm, white above the narrow, often disappearing ring, and covered with ochre-yellow granules beneath it. Spores amyloid. Occurs under coniferous trees; August to November; frequent.

Amanita fulva

left
Lepiota procera
right
Lepiota cristata

*Cystoderma
amianthinum*

Armillaria (Armillariella) mellea Honey Agaric **. Cap 5—15cm across, varying in colour from yellowish deep buff or honey-coloured to tawny or sepia, convex, later flattening and eventually with a depression, covered with fairly scattered, small, honey-coloured or brownish, hairy scales which eventually tend to disappear except in the centre. Gills whitish or flesh coloured, adnate to decurrent, often brown-spotted. Stem 7·5—15cm×0·5—1cm, tawny or brownish, darkening with age, often slightly swollen towards the base which is often tinged or flecked with yellow, white above the thick, woolly, white or yellow flecked, membranous ring on its upper half. Usually in clusters which may be very large at times. Occurs under trees or on logs and stumps; July to December; very common. Rather variable in appearance and, in consequence, is subdivided by some authorities into several separate species. A serious parasite killing a wide range of trees including conifers. It spreads by black, bootlace-like cords, called rhizomorphs, which may be found between the bark and wood of attacked trees, on roots and in the soil.

Oudemansiella (Armillaria, Mucidula) mucida Slimy Beech Cap *. Cap 3—8cm across, white, slightly greyish, or tinged brownish, convex, later flattening, very slimy or glutinous, rather translucent; margin sometimes striate. Gills white, broad, adnate or adnexed with a decurrent tooth and well-spaced. Stem 4—7·5cm×4—15mm, white, striate above the white, horizontal or drooping, membranous ring on its upper half, somewhat scaly below it, rather tough and fibrous. Occurs on living or dead beech trunks or branches, often high up a tree and often many together; August to November; common. Also illustrated on the back cover.

White or pale spored agarics without ring or volva   Key to genera:

1a   Stem thick or thickish, mostly over 5mm wide, fleshy or fibrous.

    2a   Gills adnexed or adnate

        Oudemansiella,   Collybia,   Laccaria,   Marasmius,   Flammulina, Asterophora pages 72—78

    2b   ↓ Gills sinuate or emarginate

        Collybia maculata page 72

        Tricholoma, Lyophyllum, Lepista, Tricholomopsis, Melanoleuca pages 78—82

    2c   Gills decurrent

        Clitocybe, Cantharellula, Hygrophoropsis pages 84—86

1b   Stem slender, mostly under 5mm wide, cartilaginous or tough see page 86

Oudemansiella (Collybia) radicata Rooting Tough Shank. Cap 3—10cm across, yellow-brown to brownish olive, convex, later flattening and slightly umbonate, radially wrinkled or furrowed, slimy. Gills white, adnexed or becoming free, broad, rather thick and widely spaced. Stem 10—20cm×5mm, white or, especially below, coloured like the cap but paler, tapering upwards, fibrous and slightly cartilaginous at the surface, with a long, root-like base below the soil. Occurs under broad-leaved trees especially beech; June to November; common.

Collybia Tough Shanks. Characterized by the tough, fibrous stems, the surface layer being somewhat cartilaginous, and by the cap margin incurved when young. The gills are usually adnexed or adnate (emarginate in *C. maculata*).

Collybia maculata Spotted Tough Shank. Entirely white but becoming spotted

Armillaria mellea

left
*Oudemansiella
mucida*

right
*Oudemansiella
radicata*

Collybia maculata

with dull reddish brown. Cap 7—12cm across, flattened convex. Gills cream, emarginate, narrow, very closely spaced, margins often toothed. Stem 7—12cm × 1—2cm, thickest in the middle and narrowing downwards, striate or furrowed lengthwise, hard and tough. Taste bitter. Occurs in woods, especially pine and beech; July to November; common.

Collybia fusipes Spindle Shank. Cap 4—10cm across, dark reddish brown or liver-coloured when moist, pale dull yellowish brown when dry, strongly convex, later flattening and more or less umbonate; margin inrolled. Gills whitish, later pale reddish brown, often spotted, adnexed, becoming free, broad, widely spaced and connected by veins at their bases. Stem 7—15cm × 1cm, coloured as the cap or paler or partly whitish, swollen in the middle, furrowed lengthwise, often twisted, tough and fibrous, the surface tissues somewhat cartilaginous, narrowing to a thin stalk at the base which arises from a mass of tissue. Grows in tufts at bases of broad-leaved trees, especially beech and oak; May to December; frequent.

Collybia butyracea Buttery Tough Shank. Cap 5—8cm across, bay to smoky- or dingy olive-brown when moist, paling to almost white from the margin inwards as it dries, hygrophanous with a sharp boundary between the wet and dry portions, the centre remaining dark longest, convex, later flattening, more or less umbonate, smooth and greasy. Gills white, slightly adnexed or free, broad and closely spaced; edges notched. Stem 5—8cm × 0·5—1cm, reddish brown or sepia, narrowing upwards from the swollen, white woolly base, striate and fibrous; surface tissues somewhat cartilaginous. Occurs in broad-leaved and coniferous woods; common in autumn but may be found all the year round.

Collybia (*Marasmius*) *dryophila* Oak Tough Shank. Cap 2—4cm across, pale yellowish with a tinge of brown in the centre, or light to dark dull yellowish or orangy brown, flattened shallow convex to flat and with a shallow depression, smooth. Gills white or pale yellowish, adnexed or free, narrow and closely spaced. Stem 4—7cm × 2—4mm, yellowish to reddish brown, surface tissues somewhat cartilaginous; base prolonged into a short root. Occurs in woods, especially of oak; May to November; very common.

Collybia (*Marasmius*) *peronata* Wood Woolly Foot. Cap 3—6cm across, yellowish, reddish or pale greyish-purplish brown, drying paler, rather thin-fleshed, pliant and somewhat leathery, often wrinkled and streaked; margin sometimes striate. Gills cream to yellow-brown or reddish brown, adnexed, becoming free, closely spaced. Stem 5—9cm × 2—6mm, whitish to yellowish or brownish, tapering upwards, densely clothed with long, yellowish or whitish, more or less felted or woolly hairs towards the base, which is often curved. The basal mycelium often binds dead leaves together. Taste acrid. Odour faintly of vinegar with mint. Occurs singly or in small groups in woods especially under broad-leaved trees; August to November; very common.

Collybia (*Marasmius*) *confluens* is somewhat similar, but is more slender and lacks the woolly covering of the base of the stem; it usually grows in clusters. It has a greyish flesh-coloured to almost white cap and the stem is a deeper flesh colour or has a purplish tinge and is downy (not woolly) with short hairs. Occurs under broad-leaved trees, especially beech; June to December; common.

Collybia fusipes

Collybia butyracea

Collybia dryophila

Collybia peronata

Marasmius Mummy caps. Characterized by a rather tough consistency and the ability to dry out and then revive on wetting. The difference between these and certain species of *Collybia* is not clear cut and some, for example *C. peronatus* and *C. confluens*, are sometimes placed in *Marasmius*. Some species are small and have thin, tough stems and are dealt with later in this book (see page 92).

Marasmius oreades Fairy-ring Champignon **. Cap 2—6cm across, pale reddish brown when moist, becoming buff to pale yellowish brown when dry, hygrophanous with a sharp line between the wet and dry parts, convex, later flattening and slightly umbonate; margin grooved when old. Gills pallid white to pale buff, free, broad and well-spaced. Stem 4—10cm × 2—4mm, pale buff and tough. Spores pale yellowish in the mass. Often grows in rings on lawns and grassland, these being visible due to the poor growth of the grass on them even when the fruit-bodies are absent. May to November; common.

Flammulina (Collybia) velutipes Velvet Shank *. Cap 2—10cm across, bright yellow-ochre with tawny centre, smooth and very slimy, convex, later flattening, sometimes somewhat irregular; margin finally slightly striate. Gills whitish to pale yellowish, later becoming deeper in colour, adnexed, broad and widely spaced. Stem 5—10cm × 4—8mm, lemon-yellow, later umber to blackish and densely velvety at the base or for up to the entire length, tough, the superficial tissues more or less cartilaginous. Usually occurs in clusters, sometimes in large numbers, on trunks of broad-leaved trees, logs, branches, etc., in winter; November to March; common. If eaten the stems should be discarded.

Laccaria Very like *Collybia* and distinguished from it mainly by the shortly spined spores. Formerly included in *Clitocybe* but the gills differ as they are adnate with a decurrent tooth, instead of decurrent.

Laccaria laccata The Deceiver *. Cap 3—5cm across, reddish brown or tawny to brick-red when moist, paling to ochre-yellow or dull yellowish when dry, hygrophanous, with a sharp distinction between moist and dry regions, convex, later flattening, sometimes umbilicate; surface often breaking up into small, scurfy scales; margin often waved and crisped, striate when moist. Gills mauvy pinkish, white-powdered when mature, adnate with a decurrent tooth, broad and well spaced. Stem 5—10cm × 6—10mm, the same colour as the cap or darker, often longitudinally streaked, fibrous, toughish, curved and twisted; base white and woolly. Occurs in woods and on heaths; July to December; one of the commonest of agarics. Very variable in appearance and often difficult to recognize at first sight, hence the common name, but a glance at the gills, which have a peculiar colour shade and pattern that once known is easily remembered, is usually sufficient to identify it. *L. proxima* * is very similar but tends to be larger and taller and grows in damper places. Its spores are oval instead of spherical as in the last species.

Laccaria amethystea (*laccata* var. *amethystina*). The Amethyst Agaric *. Very similar to *L. laccata* but the whole fungus is a beautiful deep violet or amethyst, drying paler. Intermediate forms between the two species occur.

Marasmius oreades

Flammulina velutipes

Laccaria laccata

Laccaria amethystea

Asterophora (*Nyctalis*) *parasitica* Pick-a-back Toadstool. Cap 1·5—3cm across, whitish, later grey or tinged lilac, bell-shaped, later convex, silky. Gills whitish, adnate or decurrent by a tooth, thick, widely spaced and alternately long and short. They become crumpled and covered with a pale brownish dust of 'chlamydospores', a special type of spore similar in nature to conidia. Stem 2·5—6cm × 2—4mm, white, slender, often curved and hairy at the base. Occurs often in clusters on old, decaying specimens of *Russula densifolia, R. foetens, R. delica* and *Lactarius vellereus* on which it is parasitic; June to December; frequent. *A. lycoperdoides* is rather similar, but the cap becomes covered with a fawn powder of chlamydospores instead of the gills, and the fungus grows on old specimens of *Russula nigricans.*

Tricholoma Formerly included all white spored agarics with sinuate or emarginate gills and fleshy stems. Several genera have now been separated from it on various grounds, but are macroscopically very similar. They include *Tricholomopsis, Lepista, Lyophyllum* and *Melanoleuca.* Note that *Collybia maculata* (page 72) has emarginate gills and might therefore be mistaken for a *Tricholoma.*

Tricholoma (*Calocybe*) **gambosum** St. George's Mushroom **. Cap 5—15cm across, whitish to pale buff, convex, later flattening and often more or less wavy, smooth and thick-fleshed. Gills whitish to pale buff, sinuate or adnexed, with a slight decurrent tooth, broadest in the middle of their length and closely spaced. Stem 5—10cm × 1—3cm, whitish or buff tinted, cylindrical, often curved at the base, solid with close-textured, not fibrous, flesh. May occur singly or two to three together, but often forms arcs or rings. Taste and odour mealy. Occurs on grassland, in hedges or in woods on limestone or chalk in spring; April to June; frequent.

Tricholoma saponaceum Soap-scented Tricholoma. Cap 3—8cm across, rather variable in colour, dull greyish brown, dark greyish, olive-grey or olive, convex, later flattening, often more or less irregular, sometimes umbonate, smooth or somewhat scaly. Gills white, sometimes with a greenish blue tint, becoming spotted reddish, sinuate and well-spaced. Stem 5—10cm × 1·5—2cm, whitish or pallid whitish, tapering below, often curved; surface with small fibres or scales that may be dark coloured. Flesh often tinged reddish in places, especially in stem base. Odour of kitchen soap. Yellowish and white varieties occur. Occurs in both broad-leaved and coniferous woods, August to November; frequent.

T. portentosum ** has a greyish brown cap 6—10cm across, streaked with fibrils and with an almost black centre. The gills are white, later a faint yellow and the stem is white, tinged sulphur and stout. Occurrs under pines, September to November; occasional.

Tricholoma argyraceum (*T. scalpturatum*) *. Cap 5—7cm across, whitish, pale grey, mouse-grey or pale brownish, convex, later flattening and often umbonate, with few to many fibrous, flattened, darker to umber scales; margin often felty. Gills white or greyish, becoming yellow or spotted with yellow, sinuate to almost free and closely spaced. Stem 3—7cm × 8—12mm, whitish, cylindrical or tapering at the base, with closely adhering fibrils and more or less hollow. Taste mealy. Occurs in broad-leaved woods, especially beech on chalk, but also under conifers; August to November; frequent.

*Asterophora
parasitica*

*Tricholoma
gambosum*

*Tricholoma
saponaceum*

*Tricholoma
argyraceum*

Tricholoma sciodes Cap 5—7cm across, sepia or greyish, usually tinted with lilac, violet or sometimes carmine-rose, convex, sometimes slightly lumpy; surface breaking up into sparse, flat, concentrically arranged, scales. Gills grey, emarginate, broad and well-spaced; edge often blackish or with black spots. Stem 5—10cm×14—17mm, greyish; surface slightly woolly. Taste slowly hot. Occurs under broad-leaved trees, especially beech; August to November; frequent. *T. virgatum* is very similar and has the same hot taste, but the cap is conical at first and later convex with a pointed umbo. The surface contains numerous, darker, radiating fibres. The gills are white and rarely have a blackish edge while the stem is longer and narrower, being 8—12mm wide. Occurs in coniferous woods; November; less frequent.

    T. terreum is another similar species that occurs under conifers and differs in not having a hot taste. The cap is umbonate, scaly, mouse-grey to brownish black and has dark fibres. The gills are whitish, later grey and the stem is white or grey with a white, mealy top. August to November, occasional. *T. pardinum* (*T. tigrinum*) †† is noteworthy since it is very poisonous. It is large, the cap being 9—20cm across, grey, lilac-grey or grey-brown, woolly and splitting up into concentrically arranged scales; gills whitish; stem whitish 4—10cm×1·5—3cm; taste mealy. It is rather rare and occurs under both broad-leaved and coniferous trees in mountainous regions and is absent from Britain.

Tricholoma sulphureum Sulphurous Tricholoma. Entirely sulphur-yellow. Cap 4—8cm across, the centre sometimes dull reddish brown, convex, later flattening and slightly umbonate, sometimes slightly irregular, silky then smooth. Gills emarginate, rather thick and well-spaced. Stem 5—11cm×1cm, cylindrical or tapering downwards, often curved, fibrous, finally hollow. Odour peculiar, suggesting coal gas. Occurs in broad-leaved woods, especially under oaks; September to November; frequent.

Tricholoma fulvum (*T. flavobrunneum*). Cap 5—10cm across, reddish brown to chestnut, often darker at the centre, with darker, radial streaks, slimy. Gills pale yellow, blotched or spotted with reddish brown when old or after handling, emarginate and closely spaced. Stem 7·5—12cm×12mm, often narrowing both upwards and downwards, reddish brown and streaked with fibres. Flesh white in the cap, yellow in the stem and distinguished from other brown species of *Tricholoma* by this colour. Odour of rancid meal. Occurs in broad-leaved woods especially under birches and on acid soils; September to November; frequent. *T. ustale* is rather similar having a slimy bay-brown cap and gills that become spotted red-brown but it lacks the rancid mealy odour and the stem flesh is not yellow. It is uncommon and grows in broad-leaved woods especially of beech.

Tricholomopsis Only differs from *Tricholoma* microscopically by having distinctively-shaped cells called cystidia on the gill edge.

Tricholomopsis (*Collybia, Tricholoma*) *platyphylla* Broad-gilled Agaric. Cap 5—12cm across, brownish grey to dark smoky brown, watery when moist and streaked with fibres, slightly convex to rather flat, thin-fleshed. Gills white or tinged the same colour as the cap, very broad and cut off obliquely next to the stem. Stem 7—12cm×1—2cm, white, cylindrical; surface covered with small fibres; base attached to white cords in the soil. Occurs in broad-leaved woods; May to November; common.

*Tricholoma
sciodes*

*Tricholoma
sulphureum*

Tricholoma fulvum

*Tricholomposis
platyphylla*

Tricholomopsis (*Tricholoma*) *rutilans* Strawberries and Custard Agaric. Cap 5—16cm across, densely covered with reddish-purple downy scales between which the yellow ground colour shows, at first broadly bell-shaped, later flattened convex and often umbonate. Gills sulphur to golden yellow, broad and closely spaced; edge often slightly woolly. Stem 6—9cm×1—2·5cm, cylindrical or tapering downwards, pale yellow with a light to fairly dense sprinkling of small, purple, downy scales. Occurs on or near pine stumps; August to November; common.

Lepista Differs from *Tricholoma* by the spores being prickly under the microscope and a pale dirty pink in the mass.

Lepista (*Tricholoma, Rhodopaxillus*) *nuda* Wood Blewit **. Cap 7—10cm across, bluish lilac or lavender when young, later becoming more dull and tinged reddish brown especially in the middle, becoming paler when dry, flattened convex, later flatter or with a depression and often wavy, smooth, moist, often becoming water-soaked. Gills pale bluish lilac, becoming paler, rounded near the stem and with a decurrent tooth, closely spaced. Stem 5—9cm×1·5—2·5cm pale lavender, cylindrical and solid; surface with small fibres but mealy at the top of the stem. Spores pale dull pinkish when in a thick layer. Occurs in woods, hedges and gardens; October to December; common.
L. saevum (*personatum*), Blewits **, is rather similar but the cap is pale dull yellowish brown, buff or greyish. The gills are dirty white or tinged flesh colour while the stem is covered with lilac to violet fibrils. Occurs mainly in grass, often in rings, sometimes in woods or hedges; October to December; frequent.

Lyophyllum Species now placed in this genus were formerly allocated to *Tricholoma, Collybia* and *Clitocybe* according to the gill attachment but have in common the microscopic character that the basidia contain minute granules which stain in the dye acetocarmine.

Lyophyllum decastes (*Tricholoma* or *Lyophyllum aggregatum* var. *typicum*) *. The fruit-bodies grow in large tufts. Cap 6—15cm across, grey-brown to yellowish brown, often blotched, convex, later flattening and umbonate and often with a depression; margin often wavy and lobed. Gills white, later straw-coloured, adnate to slightly decurrent and closely spaced. Stem 8—10cm× 1·5cm, whitish to greyish, reddish brown below, sometimes attached towards one side of the cap, curved, sometimes swollen or narrowing downwards, fibrous and rather tough. Occurs in woods or gardens and on compost or sawdust heaps; July to October; frequent. Several variants are ranked either as varieties or species: *L. loricatum* has a smaller, sepia cap and in *L. fumosum* it is palish grey-brown and the gills are grey. *L. connatum* * is clearly a distinct species and is entirely white with narrow, closely-spaced, decurrent gills. It is distinguished from rather similar, poisonous species of *Clitocybe* by turning violet when rubbed with iron alum. Occurs in grass by paths in woods; September to December; uncommon.

Melanoleuca Distinguished from *Tricholoma* by the warted spores which turn violet-black with iodine solutions, the more fibrous stem and the possession of cystidia, which are distinctively-shaped cells on the gills.

Melanoleuca (*Tricholoma*) *melaleuca* *. Cap 4—10cm across, dark brown when moist, paler when dry (hygrophanous), convex, later flattening, umbonate, smooth. Gills white, emarginate, broad and closely spaced. Stem 5—8cm×5—8mm, whitish with brown fibres running lengthwise, solid; flesh fibrous. Occurs in woods; August to November; occasional.

*Tricholomopsis
rutilans*

Lepista nuda

*Lyophyllum
decastes*

*Melanoleuca
melaleuca*

Clitocybe Easily recognized amongst white-spored agarics by the more or less decurrent gills, which do not produce milk on wounding as in *Lactarius*, and the fleshy stems. *Cantharellula* differs in having amyloid spores.

Clitocybe clavipes Club-footed Clitocybe. Cap 4—6cm across, pale smoky brown to umber, sometimes with olive tinge, darker in the centre, convex, soon flat. Gills cream to pale primrose, deeply decurrent, well-spaced and thin. Stem 4—6cm×1cm, coloured as the cap but paler, club-shaped, the thick part at the base, fragile and fibrillose. Occurs in broad-leaved and coniferous woods, especially under beech; September to November; frequent. Easily recognized by the club-shaped stem and strongly decurrent, yellowish gills.

Clitocybe nebularis Clouded Agaric ?*. Cap 7·5—20cm across, pale cloudy grey, sometimes brownish grey, darker when young and also towards the centre, convex, later flattening or with a depression, at first with a bloom, later smooth, fleshy. Gills whitish, sometimes becoming yellowish grey, shortly decurrent, very closely spaced and thin. Stem 7—12cm×2—3cm, coloured like the cap but paler, often narrowing upwards, somewhat swollen towards the base, fibrillose, breaking easily. Occurs in both broad-leaved and coniferous woods; August to November; common. Although eaten and enjoyed by many, it disagrees with some, so should just be sampled in small amounts only.

Clitocybe geotropa, the Rickstone Agaric **, is an allied but rather taller species recognized by the prominent, rounded-conical umbo. The cap is 3—20cm across, and brownish buff. The gills are the same colour and decurrent, while the stem is slightly paler, 5—12cm×2—3cm and widens towards the base. Occurs in clearings in woods or grassland, sometimes in rings; September to November; occasional.

Clitocybe infundibuliformis Common Funnel Cap *. Cap 3—6cm across, pale buff to pale dull yellowish or sienna brown, funnel-shaped, thin fleshed and silky; margin incurved at first. Gills whitish, strongly decurrent and closely spaced. Stem 3—8cm×4—8mm, coloured like the cap or slightly darker, hairy and slightly swollen below. Flesh rather tough and white. Spores smooth under the microscope. Occurs in woods, in grass or on heaths; July to November; common.

Clitocybe flaccida (*C. inversa*) Tawny Funnel Cap **. Cap 5—10cm across, orangy brown or tawny to palish rusty, more or less funnel-shaped, smooth, leathery; edge often wavy or lobed. Gills white to yellowish, deeply decurrent, narrow and closely spaced. Stem 2·5—5cm×0·5—1cm, coloured like the cap or paler, smooth above, thicker below and white woolly, often curved, becoming hollow. Flesh pale dull yellowish brown. Spores minutely rough under the microscope. Occurs sometimes in clusters or in rings, in broad-leaved and coniferous woods; September to December; frequent.

Clitocybe odora, the Blue-green Clitocybe, is easily recognized by its blue-green cap, 5—9cm across, the stem and gills being tinged the same colour. It has a strong aniseed-like odour and is used for flavouring. Occurs in broad-leaved woods; August to November; fairly frequent. *C. fragrans* has the same odour, but is small and pale greyish brown to whitish. It is a hygrophanous species with a cap 2—4cm across and grows in grass and moss in broad-leaved woods in late autumn. *C. vibecina* and *C. langei* are brown, hygrophanous, woodland species recognized by their mealy odour, but may only be reliably distinguished by their spore shapes.

Clitocybe clavipes

Clitocybe nebularis

Clitocybe infundibuliformis

Clitocybe flaccida

Clitocybe dealbata ††. Cap 2—4cm across, white or tinged yellowish brown, flattened convex; surface matt. Gills white, closely spaced, slightly decurrent. Stem 2·5—3·5cm × 8—10mm, whitish, white and mealy at the top. Odour mealy. Occurs in grassland; July to November; frequent. *C. rivulosa* †† is very similar, but more dull in colour. The cap is at first silky white, but soon becomes greyish flesh-coloured to yellowish or brownish and is wavy or lobed. It lacks the mealy odour of the last, but grows in similar places, often in company with *Marasmius oreades*, so when gathering the latter for the pot, great care should be taken not to include the former since it is deadly poisonous. *C. cerussata* †† is another white, but larger, more fleshy species that is also poisonous. It grows in coniferous woods and has a cap 5—8cm across with a white silkiness giving it an appearance of having been painted with white lead. This disappears later but the cap remains white. The spore deposit is pure white. It somewhat resembles *Lyophyllum connatum* but does not turn violet with iron salts or alum. *C. phyllophila* †† is very similar but grows in broad-leaved woods and the spore deposit is pale ochre-clay coloured.

Cantharellula cyathiformis The Goblet *. Cap 2—7cm across, dark greyish brown to umber or sienna when moist, paler when dry, hygrophanous, cup- or funnel-shaped, thin-fleshed; margin incurved. Gills smoky grey, adnate to decurrent, well-spaced and sometimes branching. Stem 5—10cm × 6—9mm, the same colour as the cap or paler, tapering upwards, covered with a network of fibrils; base white and downy. Spores amyloid. Occurs in woods and on grassland; September to January; frequent in late autumn.

Hygrophoropsis (*Clitocybe, Cantharellus*) *aurantiacus* False Chantarelle. Cap 2—8cm across, orange-yellow to orange, sometimes paler and browner, convex with a central depression to more or less funnel-shaped, often wavy; surface slightly downy; margin incurved. Gills deep orange, sometimes paler, decurrent, thin, closely spaced, repeatedly forked and narrow. Stem 3—5cm × 6—8mm, the same colour as the cap or reddish brown, sometimes dark brown below, curved. The spores turn red-brown with iodine solutions. It resembles *Cantharellus cibarius* but has true, plate-like gills not merely rounded folds or ridges. Occurs under conifers; August to November; common. Edibility doubtful, probably best avoided.

White or pale spored agarics with slender, tough or cartilaginous stems Key to genera:

1a Cap margin incurved when young   *Collybia* page 86,
        Pseudohiatula page 88 (see also *Laccaria* and *Flammulina* page 76)
1b Cap margin straight when young.
    2a Gills adnexed, adnate or sinuate
                                    Mycena page 88, *Marasmius* page 92
    2b Gills decurrent   *Omphalina* page 94

Collybia cirrhata Cap 5—10mm across, white with yellowish or brownish centre, later flat, very thin. Gills white, adnate, narrow and closely spaced. Stem 2—3cm × 1mm, whitish, with a tapering root. In troops on moss or decaying remains of agarics; August to November; fairly common. *C. cookei* differs in that the stem arises from a small, yellowish, tuber-like body, whereas *C. tuberosa* has a reddish-brown to blackish tuber.

Clitocybe dealbata

*Cantharellula
cyathiformis*

*Hygrophoropsis
aurantiacus*

Collybia cirrhata

Pseudohiatula (*Strobilurus, Collybia, Marasmius*) *tenacella* Spring Pine-cone Toadstool. Cap 1—3cm across, date-brown, sienna or yellowish brown to pale ochre or even paler, flattened convex, later flatter, smooth and matt. Gills white, adnexed, narrow and closely spaced. Stem 3—8cm×2—3mm, pale buff to whitish and minutely granular towards the top, yellowish ochre to date-brown below and often wavy. The stem base passes down into the soil like a long, slender, narrowing root which with care may sometimes be traced to a pine cone buried up to 10cm in the soil. Taste slightly bitter. Spores not amyloid. Occurs under pines; April to May; fairly common. *Baeospora* (*Collybia*) *myosura* is rather similar and also grows on buried pine cones, but is a winter fungus, the taste is not bitter, the gills are very closely spaced and the spores are amyloid. *Pseudohiatula eculenta* is again similar but grows on the cones of Douglas Fir and spruce.

Mycena Helmet caps. A large genus of medium to very small agarics often with conical, bell-shaped or parabolic, straight-edged caps characterized by their thin, cartilaginous stems.

Mycena galericulata Bonnet Mycena. Cap 2—8cm across, grey-brown, sometimes yellowish brown or paler, rounded conical or bell-shaped at first, soon flattening, broadly umbonate, striate to the umbo. Gills at first white, becoming pale dull pinkish with age, adnate with a decurrent tooth, fairly widely spaced, with veins connecting their bases (i.e. where they are attached to the cap). Stem 5—12cm×3—5mm, the same colour as the cap, smooth, appearing as if polished, cartilaginous, often curved at the base, hollow, breaking easily; base hairy and rooting. Spores amyloid. Occurs in clusters on dead wood, stumps, etc. of broad-leaved trees; throughout the year but mainly in late autumn; very common.

Mycena alcalina Cap 2—5cm across, dark sooty brown, bell-shaped, later convex with a prominent umbo, strongly striate when moist. Gills grey or grey-brown, with a whitish edge, adnate or somewhat sinuate and not connected by veins. Stem 5—8cm×2—4mm, the same colour as the cap, smooth and shining, cartilaginous, hairy towards the base and somewhat rooting. Odour characteristic, suggesting nitric acid or ammonia. Spores amyloid. Occurs in tufts on and around stumps, mainly of conifers; August to October and May to June; fairly common. *M. leptocephala* (*ammoniaca*) has the same odour but is a more slender agaric not growing in tufts on wood but in grass on lawns and in fields; July to November; fairly common.

Mycena pura Lilac Mycena. Cap 2—8cm across, typically various shades of lilac but varying to rose-pink, broadly bell-shaped, later flattening; margin striate. Gills whitish to pink, adnate with a decurrent tooth, broad; bases connected by veins. Stem 3—10cm×2—6mm, the same colour as the cap or paler, smooth, polished, cartilaginous, hollow; base white-woolly. Odour and taste of radish. Spores amyloid. Occurs amongst dead leaves in woods, especially of beech; May to December; common. *M. pelianthina* is somewhat similar and has the same odour, but it is easily recognized as the margins of the gills are dark purple-violet. The fruit-body is more squat with the stem compared to the cap diameter being proportionally shorter. The cap is also flatter. Occurs in beech woods; August to November; uncommon.

Pseudohiatula
tenacella

Mycena
galericulata

Mycena alcalina

Mycena pura

Mycena inclinata Cap 2—4cm across, red-brown, dingy brown or grey, hemispherical or broadly conical, later shallow convex with shallow, broad umbo, striate nearly to the centre; margin slightly exceeding the gills, somewhat scalloped and often with small, rounded teeth. Gills whitish, later pinkish or greyish, adnates with a decurrent tooth and closely spaced. Stem 6—10cm× 2—4mm, whitish above, but bright orangy brown lower down and chestnut towards the base, shining, cartilaginous, hairy below, often twisted or curved; base rooting. Odour and taste rancid. Spores amyloid. Occurs in dense tufts on dead wood or stumps of oak and sweet chestnut; August to November; frequent.

Mycena galopus Milk-drop Mycena (or Helmet Cap), Cap 1—2cm across, rounded conical, hemispherical or bell-shaped, greyish to pale fawn with the centre often umber, striate almost to centre. Gills whitish to greyish, adnexed and fairly closely spaced. Stem 5—10cm×1—2mm, greyish to sooty brown, whitish at the top, exuding a white milk when cut or broken, cartilaginous; base thicker, white-woolly. Spores amyloid. Occurs on the ground, often in troops, in woods, hedgerows, etc.; August to December; very common. Var. *candida* is pure white. *M. leucogala* is very similar but is black or very dark brown and favours burnt places.

Mycena polygramma Steely-stemmed Mycena (or Helmet Cap). Fruit-body tall. Cap 2—5cm across, ash-grey or grey-brown with a whitish bloom at first; furrowed at the margin. Gills white to greyish or pinkish, adnexed to free and well-spaced. Stem 6—10cm×2—4mm, silvery or bluish-grey with numerous, fine, parallel grooves running lengthwise, cartilaginous, rigid; base hairy and rooting. Spores amyloid. Easily recognized by the grooved stem. Occurs on the ground or on branches or stumps under broad-leaved trees; June to December; fairly common.

Mycena epipterygia, the Yellow-stemmed Mycena, is easily recognized by the yellow colour of its slimy stem and the slimy, gelatinous skin which may be pulled off the cap. It is common on heaths and in woods under birches or conifers; August to November.

Mycena sanguinolenta Small Bleeding Mycena. Cap 4—20mm across, brownish red, often with purple tint, or paler, umbo darker, hemispherical, conical bell-shaped, later flattening and umbonate, striate when moist; margin minutely toothed. Gills whitish to flesh coloured, adnate; edge dark reddish brown. Stem 5—8cm×1mm, pale to reddish, very slender and rather weak, cartilaginous, exuding a blood-red juice when broken or cut; base hairy, often with long root-like threads attached. Occurs on the ground in woods, solitary; August to November; very common. *M. haematopus*, the Bleeding Mycena, is larger and more robust and the stem also exudes a blood-red fluid when cut. The cap is 1—3cm across, bell-shaped to convex and is grey-brown with a purple tint to deep brownish red. The stem is 5—10cm×2—3mm and white, grey or tinted purplish. It grows in tufts on dead wood of broad-leaved trees; August to November; frequent.

Mycena inclinata

left
Mycena galopus
right
Mycena polygramma

Mycena sanguinolenta

Mycena (*Omphalia, Omphalina*) *fibula* Carpet-pin Mycena. Cap 5—10mm across, convex, later flattening to slightly umbilicate, light orange to almost white, striate and somewhat translucent. Gills white to pale yellow, arched, broad and decurrent. Stem 2—4cm×1mm, more or less the same colour as the cap, deeper below, downy with a hairy base and slender. Spores not amyloid. Occurs, often in troops, in moss and grass in damp places; May to November; common. *M. swartzii* is very similar and occurs in the same places, but the stem apex, and often also the centre of the cap, is dark violet and the colours elsewhere are browner.

Mycena acicula is another small, bright coloured species. It has an orange-vermilion cap, 2—10mm across and a bright yellow stem 2—5cm×1mm. It is fairly frequent on woody fragments, twigs, etc., in May to October.

Marasmius The thin-stemmed species are dealt with here; for the characteristics of the genus see page 76.

Marasmius (*Androsaceus*) *androsaceus* Horsehair Toadstool. Cap 4—10mm across, whitish to pale smoke or reddish brown, centre darker, flattish, umbilicate, radially wrinkled, thin and paper-like, striate. Gills whitish or dirty flesh coloured, adnate, closely spaced and narrow. Stem 3—6cm×1mm, thread-like, black, horny and often bent and twisted when dry, tough, arising from black, horsehair-like mycelial strands. Occurs on dead leaves, twigs, conifer needles and the stems of heather; May to November; common.

Marasmius ramealis Twig Mummy Cap. Cap 6—15mm across, whitish, reddish in the centre, convex, later flattened or with a depression, often somewhat wrinkled and thin-fleshed. Gills white, adnate, narrow and well-spaced. Stem 6—10cm×1—2mm, whitish or tinged reddish below, slender, curving upwards from the base; surface mealy. Often occurs in large numbers growing along the lengths of twigs or bramble stems in woods; June to October; common.

Marasmius (*Androsaceus*) *rotula* Little Wheel Toadstool. Cap 5—15mm across, white or cream, sometimes with greyish centre, convex, later flattened, umbilicate, with radiating furrows like an umbrella, flesh thin and papery; margin scalloped. Gills white and attached to a collar which encircles the top of the stem but is not attached to it. They are narrow, widely spaced and connected by veins. Stem 2—5cm×1mm, dark red-brown or blackish, horny, shining and very slender. Occurs on dead twigs, roots, etc., in woods and hedgerows; May to January; fairly common. *M. graminum* has the gills similarly attached to a collar, but the cap is red-brown and the stem deep brown. It grows on dead stems and leaves of grasses and rushes. *M. calopus* (*M. languidus* of Kühner and Romagnesi) is another small, fairly frequent species and has a whitish cap 1—1·5cm across and a reddish brown stem 2—3cm×2mm. The gills are not attached to a collar. It grows on twigs and grass stems from September to November.

Mycena fibula

*Marasmius
androsaceus*

*Marasmius
ramealis*

Marasmius rotula

Omphalina (*Omphalia*) *ericetorum* Cap 1—2cm across, usually pale olive brown but also straw-coloured, sepia, greyish or whitish, convex, later flattened with a central depression, thin-fleshed and striate nearly to the centre; margin furrowed and scalloped. Gills white, later cream or yellowish, decurrent, widely spaced, connected by veins, sometimes forked. Stem 2·5—3cm × 2mm, the same colour as the cap, slender, thickening upwards, smooth or slightly downy; base white woolly. This agaric grows in association with an alga to form the lichen *Botrydina vulgare* which produces dark green gelatinous globules around the base of the fruit-body. Occurs on peaty ground on heaths and moors or in woods; May to November; common.

Agarics with dirty pinkish to dull pinkish cinnamon spores Key to genera:

1a Stem fleshy, usually thick.
    2a Gills free   *Pluteus* page 94
    2b ↓ Gills sinuate or emarginate   *Entoloma* page 94
    2c Gills decurrent   *Clitopilus* page 96
1b Stem cartilaginous, slender   *Nolanea* page 96

Pluteus Easily recognized by the free gills, fleshy stem and pinkish spores. Some species are large and robust, whilst others are quite small. The genus *Volvariella* differs in having a cup-shaped volva at the base of the stem.

Pluteus cervinus Fawn Pluteus*. Cap 4—10cm across, light to dark umber or sepia, streaked with radially arranged fibrils within its flesh, at first broadly bell-shaped, then convex to flat, slightly slimy or sticky when moist. Gills white at first then dull flesh coloured, free, closely spaced and broad. Stem 7—10cm × 5—15mm, white, often streaked lengthwise with umber fibres, cylindrical or swollen somewhat at the base. Occurs on stumps, fallen trunks and sawdust heaps; throughout the year, but mainly May to November; common. *Volvariella* (*Volvaria*) *speciosa* *, the Pink-spored Grisette, is similar but has a paler brown to almost whitish, sticky cap, and a taller stem with a membranous, cup-shaped volva at its base. It grows on rich soil, rotting grass or straw and on compost heaps.

Entoloma Recognized by the pink spores, sinuate or emarginate (sometimes almost free) gills and the fleshy stem. Sometimes treated as a sub-genus of *Rhodophyllus*, which also includes *Leptonia*, *Nolanea* and *Eccilia*, which all share the characteristic of the spores being knobbly or angular under the microscope.

Entoloma (***Rhodophyllus***) *nidorosum* Cap 3—7cm across, greyish fawn when moist, paler to whitish when dry, convex, later flattening, thin-fleshed and fragile. Gills whitish, later flesh coloured, emarginate and almost free. Stem 5—13cm × 3—15mm, whitish, powdery at the top. Odour of nitric acid. Occurs in woods and on grassland; August to December; frequent. *E. rhodopolium* is very similar but lacks the nitrous odour and grows in woods.

Entoloma (***Rhodophyllus***) *sinuatum* (*E. lividum*) Livid Entoloma ††. Cap 7—15cm across, dirty yellowish, convex, later flattening but with slightly raised central region, fleshy, smooth, slightly sticky. Gills white at first, later flesh-coloured, emarginate to almost free, broad and well-spaced. Stem 8—14cm × 2·5—3cm, white, cylindrical, striate, top powdery. Odour faintly either of new meal, or burnt sugar or unpleasant. Occurs under broad-leaved trees, especially oak and beech; August to November; uncommon.

*Omphalina
ericetorum*

Pluteus cervinus

*Entoloma
nidorosum*

Entoloma sinuatum

Clitopilus prunulus The Miller **. Cap 3—10cm across, white, convex, later flattening or with a depression, often rather irregular, wavy and lobed, sticky when moist, sometimes spotted or concentrically banded. Gills whitish, later pale flesh coloured, deeply decurrent, narrow and closely spaced. Stem 2—6cm×1—1.5cm, white, thickest in the middle or at the top, sometimes inserted towards one side of the cap, powdery or downy. Odour and taste of new meal. Occurs in grassy places in woods and on pastures; June to November; fairly common. *Leptonia (Rhodophyllus) sericella* is a small white or yellowish white species with a convex cap, 0.5—2cm across, often with a slight depression, with the margin incurved at first and adnate gills. It is fairly common in grassland. Certain other species of the genus have bright blue or green stems or caps.

Nolanea (Entoloma, Rhodophyllus) sericea Silky Nolanea. Cap 2—4cm across, umber, becoming paler and silky when dry, convex, later flattening, slightly umbonate. Gills whitish to greyish, later dirty pink, emarginate and adnexed. Stem 2.5—5cm×3—6mm, greyish brown, whitish at the base, relatively short and slender, fibrillose. Odour of new meal. Common in grassland; May to October. Other species of *Nolanea* have the same characters as *Mycena* apart from their pinkish spores.

Agarics with rusty brown spores   Key to genera:

1a   Stem with a ring   *Pholiota, Gymnopilus, Galerina* pages 96—98
1b   ↓   No ring but a web-like cortina present when young
                                          Cortinarius page 100, *Gymnopilus* page 98
1c   Neither ring nor cortina present.
      2a   Gills free   *Bolbitius* page 102
      2b   ↓   Gills adnexed or adnate   *Galerina, Conocybe* page 98
      2c   ↓   Gills slightly decurrent   *Tubaria* page 102
      2d   Gills strongly decurrent   *Paxillus* page 102

Pholiota Used to include all brown-spored species with a ring, but now also includes ringless species and is defined by the filamentous cap skin and smooth spores without a germ pore. *Gymnopilus* has rough spores, in *Galerina* they have a germ pore, whilst in *Conocybe* the cap skin is cellular.

Pholiota squarrosa Shaggy Pholiota. Cap 3—10cm across, ochre-yellow to yellowish rusty, thickly covered with reddish brown, recurved scales, convex, later flattening and with a broad, low umbo. Gills yellowish then pale rusty, adnate with a decurrent tooth and closely spaced. Stem 6—20cm×1—2.5cm, the same colour as the cap and with similar scales below the ring but smooth above it. Ring dark brown, fibrous and torn into shreds, attached towards the top of the stem. Flesh yellowish. Grows at the base of broad-leaved trees; July to December; frequent. *P. adiposa* is similar but the cap is sticky and the scales glutinous and less numerous. It is illustrated on the title page.

Gymnopilus junonius (*Pholiota spectabilis*) Cap 5—13cm across, rich tawny or golden brown, convex, with radiating fibres or small scales incorporated into the surface; margin incurved and woolly. Gills yellow at first then rusty, adnate, sometimes with a decurrent tooth, closely spaced. Stem 6—13cm×2—3cm, coloured like the cap but paler, fubrillose and somewhat spindle-shaped. Ring yellowish but becoming rusty from the spores, membranous, spreading, and attached to the upper part of the stem. Occurs in dense tufts at the bases of stumps or trunks of broad-leaved trees; August to December; frequent.

Clitopilus prunulus

Nolanea sericea

Pholiota squarrosa

*Gymnopilus
junonius*

Gymnopilus (*Flammula*) **penetrans** Cap 5—8cm across, yellowish tawny to golden, convex, later flattening, dry and smooth except for minute fibrils. Gills whitish, later pale yellow and finally tawny, adnate to slightly decurrent, broad and closely spaced. Stem 4—7cm × 6—10mm, yellow, paler above, darkens when bruised, very fibrous; base whitish. Flesh yellowish. Taste bitter. Cortina present when young, sometimes leaving a ring of fibrils on the stem. Occurs in pine woods, on the ground or on twigs, wood chips, etc., August to November; very common.

Galerina See note under *Pholiota*. Contains species both with and without rings. There are no large species as in *Pholiota* and the cap always lacks scales.

Galerina (**Pholiota**) **mutabilis** ** Cap 3—6cm across, chestnut to date-brown when moist, drying to pale tawny ochre, hygrophanous, wet and dry parts being sharply demarcated, convex, later flattening. Gills whitish, later cinnamon, adnate-decurrent, broad and closely spaced. Stem 4—8cm × 0·5—1cm, whitish above the ring, dark brown below, rather slender, scaly at first. Ring skirt-like, membranous and attached to the upper part of the stem. Grows, often in large clumps, on stumps and logs of broad-leaved trees; April to December; common. *Galerina unicolor* (*G. marginata*) is rather similar but is more slender, has only a very narrow ring and the stem has no scales. It grows on twigs and stumps, often under conifers and frequently in tufts, but these are smaller than in the last species.

Galerina (**Galera**) **hypnorum** Moss Pixy Cap. Small, cap 6—12mm across, pale ochre-yellow, hygrophanous, hemispherical to bell-shaped, striate almost to the centre. Gills cinnamon to rusty, adnate with decurrent tooth, well-spaced. Stem 2—5cm × 1—2mm, yellow to tawny, slender. Odour mealy when crushed. Taste also mealy and this distinguishes it from all other species of *Galerina*. Occurs amongst moss in woods and on heaths and grassland; May to November; common. There are several other somewhat larger species in the genus which occur in grassland and on lawns, but mostly they require microscopic examination for their identification.

Conocybe Differs from *Galerina* by the cellular structure of the cap skin. The species are mostly taller with more conical caps. A few have a ring on the stem.

Conocybe subovalis (*C. tenera* var. *subovalis*, *Galera tenera* of many writers). Brown Cone-cap. Cap 1·5—3cm across, rusty to tawny or dull ochre when wet, dull ochre-buff to pale cinnamon when dry, rounded conical to shortly parabolic, somewhat higher than wide, not striate except when very wet, smooth, thin-fleshed and fragile. Gills cinnamon, adnate later free, narrow and closely spaced. Stem 7·5—10cm × 2mm, the same colour as the cap, slender, straight, rather fragile, striate, minutely powdery, hollow, with a small but well-defined, round, whitish bulb at the base. Occurs in grass in meadows, on road sides, in gardens and woods; April to December; common. The old, broadly conceived species *C.* (*Galera*) *tenera*, of which *C. subovalis* formed part, has now been subdivided into several, rather similar species. The name *C. tenera* is now reserved for a smaller, less robust species with a shorter more dull coloured cap which is striate almost to the centre. The stem has only a small, rather inconspicuous, oval bulb at its base.

*Gymnopilus
penetrans*

Galerina mutabilis

*Galerina
hypnorum*

*Conocybe
subovalis*

Cortinarius Web toadstools. Although this genus contains several hundred European species, and agarics belonging to it are very frequently encountered in the field, very few of the individual species are at all common. Even specialists quite frequently find their identification difficult. In consequence only a very few merit illustration in this book.

Cortinarius (*subgenus Myxacium*) *pseudosalor* Cap 3—11cm across, olive-buff or greyish-buff to ochreous yellowish with the centre reddish brown or tawny, conical-convex, later flattening but still with a strong, rounded-conical umbo; surface glutinous; margin at first sometimes violet-tinted smooth to strongly wrinkled and furrowed. Gills sometimes with violet tinge when young, later becoming dirty buff or pale brownish ochre, finally rusty ochre, adnate or adnate-decurrent, broad, sometimes with veins on the sides or between them; edge paler coloured to whitish but sometimes violet tinged when young. Stem 4·5—10cm × 7—22mm, cylindrical with a pointed base but sometimes narrowing upwards. It is white or pale violaceous and silky striate above the attachment of the cortina which leaves a slight wavy ridge on the upper half, glutinous and usually deeper purplish or bluish violet but sometimes whitish below. Occurs in both broad-leaved and coniferous woods, especially under beech; August to October; common. J. Lange describes *C. elatior* as being larger and taller with a more conical cap with the margin more strongly grooved and also a more strongly spindle-shaped stem. The gills are strongly veined and *never* have violet tints. Intermediates occur, however, and *C. pseudosalor* could perhaps best be regarded as a variety of *C. elatior*.

Cortinarius (*subgenus Dermocybe*) *semisanguineus* Cap 3—8cm across, olive-buff to ochre-buff or tawny brown, sometimes darker or reddish brown at the centre, convex later flattening and umbonate, silky, minutely fibrillose-scaly. Gills deep blood-red, becoming powdered with rusty spores, adnate, broad and closely spaced. Stem 2—11cm × 4—13mm, ochre or yellowish, with paler or white apex, slender, cylindrical, solid, fibrillose, some of the fibrils reddish brown or tawny. Occurs under birches or conifers; August to November; common. *C. cinnamomeus*, the Cinnamon Web-toadstool, is similar and occurs in the same places, but the gills are at first deep lemon or chrome-yellow and later tawny orange or bright golden red. There are several other very similar species.

Cortinarius (*subgenus Telamonia*) *armillatus* Red-banded Web-cap. Cap 4—12cm across, brick-red to pale yellowish brown, centre darker, smooth or with fibres within the surface. Gills pale cinnamon then rusty to bay, adnate, very broad. Stem 6—15cm × 1—2cm, red-brown, paler than the cap, with one to several irregular red bands, cylindrical above, fibrillose, swollen at the base and often with reddish fibrils. Occurs in broad-leaved woods, expecially under birch on heathland; August to October; frequent.

Cortinarius (*subgenus Telamonia*) *paleaceus* Cap 1·5—3cm across, umber when moist, drying fawn, conical to broadly bell-shaped, with prominent somewhat pointed umbo; surface at first with whitish, recurved fibres or tiny scales, later smooth. Gills lilac at first, then cinnamon brown, adnate. Stem 5—7·5cm × 2—3mm, brownish, the cortina leaves a whitish band and several other whitish bands are scattered down the stem. Odour of geranium when bruised. Occurs on the ground in damp woods and on heaths; September to November; frequent.

*Cortinarius
pseudosalor*

*Cortinarius
semisanguineus*

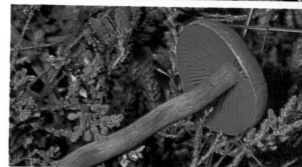

*Cortinarius
armillatus*

*Cortinarius
paleaceus*

Bolbitius vitellinus Yellow Cow-pat Toadstool. Cap 2—4cm across, chrome-yellow at first then paling to whitish, between oval and bell-shaped at first, finally almost flat, thin-fleshed, smooth at first and slimy, then drying; the margin strongly radially furrowed, very thin and often splitting. Gills cinnamon-buff to rusty, adnexed or free, broad, thin and closely spaced. Stem 6—11cm× 2—4mm, whitish or pale yellow, slender, tapering upwards, finely mealy at first and downy at the base, very fragile, hollow. Occurs on manure, straw-bales, and in grass; May to October; fairly common.

Tubaria furfuracea Cap 1—4cm across, dull orangy brown or cinnamon-brown when moist, pale dull yellowish brown when dry, hygrophanous, shallow convex, later flat, more or less scurfy; margin striate when moist, at first with smallish, white, flat scales (the remnants of the veil). Gills cinnamon-brown, broadly adnate to slightly decurrent, broad and well-spaced. Stem 2—5cm× 2—4mm, coloured as the cap or darker, covered with small, whitish scales when young, slender, hollow; base white woolly. Spore deposit rather pale coloured and ochre-tinted rather than brown. Occurs on the ground in woods, on roadsides, waste-ground and gardens; throughout the year but mainly in late autumn; common.

Paxillus Easily recognized by the rusty spores and the strongly decurrent gills which tend to have a few cross-connections where they run on to the stem and which may be easily stripped with the finger nail from the underlying flesh. The genus is more closely related to the boletes (sponge-caps) than to other agarics.

Paxillus involutus Brown Roll-rim †. Cap 7—20cm across, tawny, yellowish or olive-brown, convex at first, then flattening and with a central depression, downy, later smooth except at the margin which is strongly inrolled at first. Gills dull yellowish, later yellowish rust coloured, dingy brown where bruised, decurrent, branched and often with cross-connections near the stem, broad and closely spaced. Stem 5—8cm×1—4cm, relatively rather short, the same colour as the cap or darker, often spotted and streaked darker brown, sometimes inserted towards one side of the cap, thickening upwards. Spore deposit deep yellow-brown. Occurs in broad-leaved and coniferous woods especially on heaths; June to December; very common. It has been considered edible but although it may be consumed with impunity on one occasion, it has been reported that this produces sensitization and that on later occasions symptoms of poisoning may develop.

Paxillus atrotomentosus Cap 5—30cm across, rusty to reddish brown, flattened convex, often somewhat irregular, fleshy; surface dry and sometimes slightly woolly; margin incurved. Gills yellowish, decurrent, narrow and closely spaced, branching near the stem and often forming a network here. Stem 5—8cm×1—2·5cm, stout, surface entirely covered with dark brown, almost black 'velvet', cylindrical or narrowed at the base, often curved and usually inserted towards one side of the cap or even laterally. Spore deposit pale ochre-yellow. Occurs on or near conifer stumps; August to November; frequent.

Bolbitius vitellinus

Tubaria furfuracea

Paxillus involutus

Paxillus atrotomentosus

Agarics with dull brown spores   Key to genera:

1a   Stem with a membranous ring   *Agrocybe* page 104
1b   Membranous ring absent, gills often more or less sinuate
      2a   Cap with radiating fibres in the surface   *Inocybe* page 104
      2b   Cap surface without such fibres   *Hebeloma* page 106

Agrocybe (Pholiota) praecox Spring Agaric *. Cap 3—8cm across, whitish to
pale dirty ochre, convex, later flattening, soft. Gills whitish, later cigar-brown,
adnexed, broad and closely spaced. Stem 4—9cm×6—10mm, white, later
becoming yellowish, cylindrical; surface mealy at first. Ring white, membranous, skirt-like, striate on the upper surface and attached towards the top of
the stem. Spores cigar-brown. Taste and odour mealy. Occurs in broad-leaved
woods and in grassy places; May to July; occasional.

Agrocybe (Pholiota) erebia has a dark brown cap, 3—6cm across, umber
brown gills and a whitish to dirty brown stem with a white, skirt-like ring. It is
frequent in damp broad-leaved woods from September to November.

Inocybe Recognized by the radially arranged, sometimes silky, fibres on or in
the cap surface, the dull brown spores and the possession of a cortina.

Inocybe geophylla Common White Inocybe †. Cap 1·5—3cm across, white,
yellowish in centre, conical with an incurved margin, later bell-shaped, finally
flattening and often with a pronounced umbo, radially silky-fibrillose. Gills
whitish, later pale greyish brown, adnexed to free and closely spaced. Stem
4—8cm×2—6mm, white, silky, slender, often wavy with a small swelling at the
base. Odour peculiar, spermatic. Occurs in woods, especially in damp places;
July to December; common.

Inocybe geophylla var. lilacina Lilac Inocybe †. Only differs from the last in
being entirely lilac apart from the gills. It is rather more common and occurs in
the same places.

Inocybe fastigiata ††. Cap 3—10cm across, straw-yellow, later browner,
between conical and bell-shaped, later flattening but always umbonate, the
surface smooth but marked with radiating fibres; edge often splitting. Gills
yellowish, later olive, adnate or adnexed, narrow and closely spaced; edge
white. Stem 4—10cm×5—15mm, whitish or pale ochre, later brown, more or
less cylindrical, often wavy or curved, striate with fibrils; top white, powdery.
Odour slightly mealy. Taste slightly bitter. In broad-leaved woods especially of
beech; June to October; fairly common.

Inocybe cookei is also straw-yellow to pale ochre, but is smaller with the cap
2—4cm across, broadly conical to convex and umbonate with the surface silky-
fibrillose. The stem is 3—6cm×3—5mm and is whitish tinged with ochre and
has a small, white bulb with a rim. It occurs in broad-leaved woods; August to
November; frequent.

left
Agrocybe praecox
right
Inocybe geophylla

Inocybe geophylla
var. *lilacina*

Inocybe fastigiata

Inocybe maculata †. Cap 2—8cm across, bay to chestnut, between conical and bell-shaped, umbo often sharp, clothed with dense white fibres of the veil at first, and these may persist in patches and over the umbo; surface strongly radially fibrillose with dark brown fibres and splitting radially to show the paler flesh. Gills whitish, later snuff-brown, adnate-emarginate, narrow and closely spaced; margin white, shortly fringed. Stem 4—9cm×5—12mm, white, later brown, striate with fibrils, cylindrical; base sometimes slightly swollen. Occurs in broad-leaved woods especially of beech; September to November; frequent. *I. asterospora* † is rather similar in appearance but has a well-developed bulb with a rim at the base of the stem.

Inocybe patouillardii †. Cap 3—8cm across, white, later ivory to yellowish brown, blood-red where cracked or bruised and along the radial fibres, conical or bell-shaped, later flattening and more or less umbonate, silky fibrillose; margin often splitting. Gills white, later olive-brown, reddening when rubbed, adnate, adnexed or almost free. Stem 4—10cm×1—2cm, white, flushed red, striate with fibrils, often somewhat bulbous at the base. Occurs in broad-leaved woods, especially of beech, on limy or chalky soil; May to November; uncommon. Easily distinguished by the tendency to redden from all species of *Inocybe* except *I. godeyi* but this has a bulb with a rim on the stem and differs microscopically.

Inocybe pyriodora, the Pear-scented Inocybe, is characterized by its odour. The cap is 4—8cm across and pale ochre with reddish brown tints and has radiating brownish fibrils. *I. bongardii* has a similar odour and size, but is pale brownish and has numerous, distinct, flat, fibrous scales and also differs microscopically. Both occur in broad-leaved and coniferous woods.

Hebeloma Differs from *Inocybe* in that the cap lacks the fibres in the surface and usually in being more fleshy.

Hebeloma crustuliniforme Poison Pie †. Cap 5—10cm across, buff to pale yellowish brown, sometimes tinged reddish brown, convex, fleshy, soft and smooth, slimy at first. Gills pale milky coffee coloured, becoming date-brown, sinuate, broad and closely spaced; edge irregular and beaded with drops of moisture in damp weather. Stem 4—7cm×1—2·5cm, whitish, cylindrical, slightly swollen at the base, covered with tiny, woolly granules almost to the base so as to give it a mealy appearance. Odour of radish when bruised. Taste acrid. Occurs on damp soil in woods, gardens etc.; August to November; fairly common. *H. longicaudum* (*H. nudipes*) is similar but has a stem 7—8cm long, longer than the cap diameter. *H. sacchariolens* is a smallish species recognized by a peculiar sickly-sweet odour suggesting burnt sugar or cheap, scented soap.

Hebeloma mesophaeum Cap 2·5—4cm across, date-brown in the centre, paling to yellowish buff at the margin, convex, later flattening, smooth, slimy at first; margin with whitish fibres from the veil when young. Gills whitish to flesh-coloured, becoming dingy brown, sinuate, rather broad and closely spaced. Stem 5—7·5cm×4mm, whitish at first, later browning from the base upwards, slender and fibrillose; the veil often leaves a ring of fibrils towards the top. Flesh white in the cap, brown in the stem. Taste slightly bitter. Occurs in woods, especially of pine and birch on heaths; September to October; frequent.

Inocybe maculata

Inocybe patouillardii

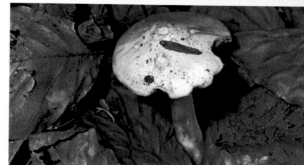

Hebeloma crustuliniforme

Hebeloma mesophaeum

Hebeloma sinapizans †. Cap 4·5—20cm across, pale umber, paling to brownish buff at the margin, convex, later flattening and wavy with the margin often turning upwards, fleshy, smooth and slightly sticky at first. Gills pale cinnamon, deeply emarginate, broad. Stem 7·5—12·5cm × 1—2cm, white, stout, cylindrical with slightly swollen base, hollow and often with a piece of flesh hanging down into the cavity; surface covered with small, recurved scales often forming irregular bands; flesh white. Odour strongly of radish. Occurs under broad-leaved trees; September to October; uncommon. *H. sinuosum* (*H. sinapizans* of J. Lange) is similar but practically odourless; flesh of stem base brown.

Agarics with either violet tinted, dark dull brown or chocolate spores Key to genera:

1a Stem with a membranous ring
    2a Gills free   *Agaricus* page 108
    2b Gills adnate to sinuate   *Stropharia* page 110
1b Stem without a membranous ring.
    3a Stem fibrous, not cartilaginous
        4a Cap with yellowish colours; cortina present when young
                                   Hypholoma page 112
        4b Cap without yellowish colours; cortina absent
                                   Psilocybe page 114
    3b Stem cartilaginous, breaking easily
                  Lacrymaria page 112, *Psathyrella* page 114

Agaricus (*Psalliota*). Includes the common mushroom and is characterized by the chocolate-brown spores, free gills and fleshy stem with a ring.

Agaricus silvaticus Brown Wood Mushroom **. Cap 7·5—11cm across, reddish to umber-brown, rounded at first then convex and finally flattened; surface densely covered with fibres and splitting into flattened scales. Gills whitish, later reddish and finally dark brown, free and closely spaced. Stem 6—9cm × 1—1·5cm, dingy white becoming brownish, fibrillose to slightly scaly below the membranous, spreading ring which is white above and greyish or brownish below. Flesh white becoming slowly pinkish, then brownish in the stem when cut or when old. Occurs in woods; July to September; fairly frequent.

Agaricus silvicola Wood Mushroom **. Cap 5—15cm across, creamy white, rounded or somewhat bell-shaped, later flattening, smooth, becoming yellow when bruised or old. Gills pale brownish violet-grey, later chocolate, free. Stem 5—15cm × 1·5—2·5cm, white, becoming yellowish brown, hollow; base bulbous. Ring membranous, broad and skirt-like, white above, with soft, brownish patches below. Flesh whitish, becoming brownish in the stem, not yellowing. Odour of aniseed. Occurs in woods, especially with conifers; August to November; fairly frequent. *A. abruptibulbus* is very similar but the bulb is flattened horizontally and the spores are smaller.

Agaricus arvensis Horse Mushroom **. Cap 7—15cm across, creamy white, bruising yellow to brown, globose, later convex and finally flattened, smooth. Gills whitish, later pale brownish violet-grey, finally chocolate, free, rather narrow. Stem 8—13cm × 1·5—3cm, white, sometimes bruising yellow, smooth, cylindrical or thickening downwards and slightly swollen at the base. Ring large and spreading, white above, with soft, radiating, brownish patches below. Flesh white, becoming tinted slightly ochre in the stem base. Odour of aniseed or almonds. In grassland, near cowsheds, etc.; July to November; frequent.

Hebeloma
sinapizans

Agaricus silvaticus

Agaricus silvicola

Agaricus arvensis

Agaricus xanthodermus Yellow-staining Mushroom †. Cap 5–10cm across, white, rapidly turning bright lemon-yellow if bruised, flattened globose, later flattened convex. Gills whitish, later pale brownish violet-grey, finally chocolate, free and closely spaced. Stem 6–10cm × 12–15mm, white, lemon-yellow when bruised, cylindrical with a somewhat bulbous base, smooth and silky; ring white and skirt-like. Flesh white, rapidly turning yellow, strongly so in stem base. Odour unpleasant, suggesting writing-ink. Occurs under trees, in hedgerows, fields, gardens, etc.; July to October; occasional. If eaten, causes violent symptoms of poisoning including vomiting and diarrhoea, but with recovery after several days; some people are unaffected. *A. placomyces* (*A. meleagris*) † is very similar, with the same yellowing, but the cap is covered with dark greyish sepia to blackish, flat, fibrous scales, especially at the centre.

Agaricus campestris Field Mushroom **. Cap 5–12cm across, white, later tinged brownish especially in the centre, convex, later flattening, smooth or with a few flattened, brownish, fibrous scales; margin incurved. Gills pink at first, later chocolate-brown, free and closely spaced. Stem 4–8cm × 2–4cm, white, bruising brownish, smooth, solid at first, but later with a narrow cavity. Ring narrow, thin and membranous, soon disappearing. Odour pleasant. Occurs in old meadows and on lawns, sometimes growing in rings; August to November; frequent. The structure is shown diagrammatically in fig. 3. The cultivated mushroom, *A. brunnescens* (*A. bisporus* var. *albida*, *A. hortensis*) is a different more robust species originating from one that grows on accumulations of organic matter such as compost heaps. If differs microscopically and also in that a thin membrane covers the base of the stem and extends up to the ring, the flesh tends to turn reddish to brownish when cut and the odour is more acid. One form has a white, smooth cap and in another it is brown and scaly.

Stropharia Distinguished from *Agaricus* by the adnate or sinuate gills and the more fibrous stem.

Stropharia aeruginosa Verdigris Toadstool †. Cap 3–8cm across, at first deep verdigris green from the coloured slime, then becoming yellowish, broadly conical or convex, later flattening, often with small, whitish scales when young, especially near the margin. Gills smoky brown, later chocolate, adnate; edge often whitish. Stem 4–10cm × 4–12mm, tinged bluish green but paler than cap, cylindrical, slimy and with small, white, cottony scales below the ring. Ring membranous and more or less horizontal at first, white above or often chocolate-coloured from the spores, bluish beneath; it soon disappears. Occurs in woods, grassland and gardens; May to November; fairly frequent.

Stropharia semiglobata Dung Roundhead. Cap 1–3cm across, pale dullish or straw-yellow, hemispherical, later convex, slimy. Gills brownish becoming chocolate, adnate, very broad and c'osely spaced. Stem 6–10cm × 2–3mm, white, later yellowish, slender, straight or curved at the base, hollow, slimy below the ring. Ring thin and narrow and often reduced to a dark line around the stem. Occurs in fields, on heaths, in woods and gardens usually on dung; throughout the year; very common.

*Agaricus
xanthodermus*

*Agaricus
campestris*

*Stropharia
aeruginosa*

*Stropharia
semiglobata*

Hypholoma Gills sinuate, sometimes adnexed. Veil present when young and cobweb-like. Cap often with a more or less yellowish coloration; stem fibrous.

Hypholoma (Naematoloma) fasciculare Sulphur Tuft†. Cap 2–5cm across, pale yellow, often reddish brown in the centre, convex, later flattening, sometimes umbonate, smooth; margin incurved, often with brownish, thin, skinny fragments of the veil. Gills greenish yellow at first, later becoming dull olive-green or chocolate, sinuate and closely spaced. Stem 5–22cm× 4–10mm, pale yellow, cylindrical, often wavy or curved, fibrillose, becoming hollow, often with a band of fibres from the veil near the top. Taste bitter. Flesh yellow, fibrous in the stem; turns orange with ammonia at the base of the stem. This reaction and the yellow gills when young distinguish it from the next species. Occurs in clusters that are often very large, on and around stumps of broad-leaved trees, all the year round though mainly in autumn; the commonest of the agarics. Also pictured on the front jacket.

Hypholoma (Naematoloma) sublateritium Brick-red Hypholoma†. Cap 3–10cm across, brick-red, yellowish or whitish towards the margin, convex, later flattening, smooth; margin incurved and often with thin, skinny fragments of the veil. Gills pale yellowish at first without greenish tinge (compare *H. fasciculare*), later greyish violet to chocolate, adnate or sinuate-adnate, rather broad and closely spaced. Stem 5–10cm×8–15mm, buffy yellowish above, reddish brown to rusty below, usually narrowing downwards, scaly-fibrillose, solid, with a ring of fibres from the veil of the upper half. Flesh yellowish, turns yellow not orange with ammonia in stem base (distinction from last species). Taste bitter. Occurs in clusters on and near stumps of broad-leaved trees; throughout the year, but mainly in autumn; fairly frequent.

Hypholoma (Naematoloma) capnoides*. Cap 2·5–8cm across, ochre-yellow, sometimes tinged tawny, paler towards the margin, brownish in centre, convex, later flattening, smooth; margin with small, skinny fragments of the veil at first. Gills whitish at first, then greyish lilac to chocolate, adnate, becoming free, fairly broad. Stem 5–7cm×4–8mm, whitish, later tinged brownish from the base up, cylindrical, often curved or wavy, initially with a few, sparse fragments from the veil. Flesh whitish or pale yellowish, rusty in stem base. Taste mild (compare last two species). Occurs in dense clumps around conifer stumps; April to December; occasional.

Lacrymaria (Hypholoma, Psathyrella) velutina (*H. lacrymabunda*) Weeping Widow†. Cap 4–7·5cm across, dull yellowish brown, broadly bell-shaped, later convex and umbonate, at first shaggy with low, radial, darker, woolly fibres, becoming smooth; margin incurved at first and fringed. Gills dark brown, tinged purplish, adnexed to sinuate-adnate, broad, closely spaced; with a white edge that exudes beads of moisture. Stem 5–12·5cm×4–15mm, the same colour as the cap but duller, paler at the top, cylindrical, fragile and hollow; with a fibrillose ring from the cortina (veil), fibrillose and scaly below this. Cortina well-developed and formed from whitish fibres, later blackened by the spores, and stretching from the cap margin to the stem, eventually disappearing. Occurs on the ground, singly or in small groups, in grassland, by road-sides, paths in wood etc.; September to December; rather frequent. The genus *Lacrymaria* is characterized by dark brown spores that are rough under the microscope.

Hypholoma
fasciculare

Hypholoma
sublateritium

Hypholoma
capnoides

Lacrymaria
velutina

Psilocybe semilanceata Liberty Cap †. Cap 1—2·5cm across, 10—15mm high, pale buff to pale, dirty, yellowish brown, darker when wet, sharply conical above, convex below, smooth, at first with a slimy skin that may be pulled off; margin incurved at first, and sometimes striate. Gills cream, later purple-black, with a white edge, narrow and ascending into the cone of the cap, adnate or adnexed and closely spaced. Stem 4—7·5cm × 2mm, the same colour as the cap but paler, whitish at the top, slender, often wavy, smooth or at first small, woolly scales, tough. Causes hallucinations if eaten. Occurs amongst grass in fields, on heaths and by roadsides, often in troops; August to December; frequent.

Psathyrella Brittle caps. Recognized by the dark brown spores, the thin, cartilaginous and brittle stems, and the caps, which are often more or less conical, having straight margins. A veil is sometimes present. If the gills are mottled lighter and darker see *Panaeolina* page 118.

Psathyrella (Hypholoma) candolleana Crumble Tuft. Cap 5—10cm across, pale honey-coloured when moist, soon whitish or tinged brownish, sometimes with a tinge of dirty violet towards the margin, hygrophanous, acorn-shaped, later bell-shaped to convex, finally flattening, thin-fleshed and fragile; surface glistening with particles under a lens; margin fringed with white, skinny fragments of the veil. Gills pale greyish lilac, later dull cinnamon, adnexed but becoming free. Stem 4—7·5cm × 4—8mm, white, somewhat thickening towards the base, slender, fragile and hollow. Occurs on and around stumps of broad-leaved trees; April to November; frequent.

Psathyrella (Hypholoma) hydrophilum Cap 3—6cm across, date-brown when moist becoming pale, dingy, yellowish brown or brownish buff, hygrophanous, globose, later convex and flattening, thin-fleshed and fragile; margin sometimes with skinny remnants of the veil. Gills whitish, becoming date-brown, adnate. Stem 5—10cm × 4—8mm, whitish, slender, smooth, fragile and hollow. Cortina of very fine threads rapidly disappearing. Grows in dense clusters on and around stumps of broad-leaved trees; August to December; common.

Agarics with black or dark olive-grey spores Key to genera:

1a Gills liquefying as fungus matures or cap strongly radially grooved
Coprinus page 114

1b Gills not liquefying, cap not strongly grooved.
    2a Gills adnate, mottled   *Panaeolus, Panaeolina* page 118
    2b Gills decurrent   *Chroogomphus* page 118

Coprinus Ink caps. Spores black. The gills liquefy starting with the margin and produce an inky fluid whilst the cap expends rapidly and flattens, the margin rolling upwards. Cap often strongly radially grooved.

Coprinus comatus Lawyer's Wig or Shaggy Ink Cap **. Cap at first white cylindrical and rounded at the top or oval, 5—15cm high, 4—6cm across, later becoming bell-shaped, the centre smooth and becoming yellow-brown, elsewhere covered with shaffy scales sometimes with brown tips; margin becoming pinkish then black, eventually splitting and rolling upwards. Gills white, later pink and finally black, free, broad and very closely spaced, dissolving into a black fluid from below upwards. Stem 12—25cm × 1—2cm, white, smooth, shining, tapering upwards, brittle and hollow; base slightly bulbous, with a short 'root'. Ring narrow, membranous, moveable, situated on the middle of the stem. Occurs in fields, on roadsides, rubbish tips, etc., often in troops or several in a cluster; April to December; common.

*Psilocybe
semilanceata*

*Psathyrella
candolleana*

*Psathyrella
hydrophilum*

Coprinus comatus

Coprinus atramentarius Common Ink Cap? *. Cap 5−8cm across, grey to grey-brown, oval, later bell-shaped or conical, up to 5cm high, slightly scaly especially in the centre, radially ribbed nearly to the centre; margin often irregularly and bluntly lobed. Gills whitish, later black, free, broad and closely spaced, dissolving into an inky fluid. Stem 7−20cm×8−18mm, white, narrowing both upwards and downwards, smooth, with an undulating ring-like mark at its widest point near the base. Occurs on the ground often near bases of trees or stumps, in woods, gardens and fields, usually clustered; May to December; common. Edible before liquefaction is advanced but causing nausea if alcoholic drink is taken at the same time.

Coprinus plicatilis Little Jap Umbrella. Cap 1−3cm across, dull pale brownish and oval at first, later rounded and broadly conical; finally almost flat, very thin and translucent, often still brownish in the centre but grey elsewhere, grooved almost to the centre and appearing as if radially pleated. Gills grey, later blackish, attached to a thickened, flattish ring of tissue around the top of the stem, narrow, widely spaced, not liquefying but withering away. Stem 2·5−7·5cm×1−2mm, whitish and somewhat translucent, slender, smooth and fragile. Solitary amongst grass on lawns, in fields or by road-sides; April to December; common. *C. hemerobius* is somewhat similar in appearance but the gills are attached to the swollen top of the stem instead of to a ring of tissue. The spore shape is also different. It occurs in grassland and woods and is uncommon.

Coprinus picaceus Magpie Ink Cap ?†. Cap 5−10cm across and up to 5cm high, oval, later bell-shaped or conical; covered with a thick, white felt when young, but this cracks into numerous white patches on a dark brown to blackish background as the cap expands. Gills white, later pinkish and finally black, free, broad and closely spaced. Stem 10−25cm×6−12mm, white, straight and rather slender, tapering upwards, smooth, fragile and hollow; base somewhat swollen and scaly. Ring absent. Usually occurs singly on the ground in broad-leaved woods especially of beech; September to December; occasional.

Coprinus micaceus Glistening Ink Cap. Cap 3−6cm across, up to 4cm high, ochre-brown to date-brown, ochre when dry, often the centre darker than the margin, oval, later somewhat bell-shaped and finally broadly conical, fragile, grooved almost to the centre, at first with a sprinkling of glittering, mealy particles if examined with a lens. Gills whitish, later becoming very dark brown, adnexed, closely spaced, eventually liquefying. Stem 5−20cm×4−8mm, white, hollow and smooth (but in a young specimen, under a lens, it is seen to be densely covered with short hairs). Occurs in clusters, which may be dense, on and near stumps of broad-leaved trees; throughout the year; common. This and several very similar species can really only satisfactorily be told apart by microscopic examination of the spores and other microscopic characteristics. They include *C. truncorum, C. domesticus, C. radians* and *C. silvaticus.*

left
*Coprinus
atramentarius*
right
Coprinus plicatilis

Coprinus picaceus

Coprinus micaceus

Coprinus (Psathyrella, Pseudocoprinus) disseminatus Trooping Crumble Cap. Cap 1—2cm across, pale dull brownish ochre or ochre buff, later greyish with the centre remaining brownish, oval at first, then approaching hermispherical, radially striate and grooved almost to centre, glistening with particles under a lens. Gills whitish, later dark grey, adnate, narrow, closely spaced and not liquefying. Stem 2·5—4cm × 2mm, white, semi-translucent often curved or wavy; base with white woolly mycelium. Occurs in large clusters or troops on old stumps or on the ground; April to November; frequent. Not a typical *Coprinus* since the gills do not liquefy and so is sometimes placed in *Psathyrella* or in a special genus *Pseudocoprinus*.

Panaeolus Mottle gills. Recognized by the black spores which do not ripen uniformly over the gill surface but in patches producing a mottled appearance.

Panaeolus sphinctrinus Cap 1—3cm across, 2—2·5cm high, dark grey or blackish, paling to lead-grey when dry, centre sometimes brownish, oval then parabolic or bell-shaped, never flattening; margin exceeding the gills and splitting into small, white teeth which disappear eventually. Gills grey to blackish, sinuate-adnate and closely spaced; edge often white. Stem 7—12cm × 2—3mm, greyish to grey-brown or almost black, slender, stiff, fragile, hollow; surface appearing powdery. Occurs in rich meadows and pastures, often on dung; May to October; fairly common. Recognized by its greyish to blackish stem and the white teeth on the cap margin.

Panaeolus semiovinus (Annelaria separata) the Egg-shell Toadstool, is recognized by the stem having a narrow, membranous ring. Its cap resembles the upper two thirds of an egg-shell and is 2—6cm across and 2·5—4·5cm high, buffy whitish to brownish buff. The ring is narrow and membranous. It grows on dung in grassland; June to November; frequent. *P. rickenii*, common in grassland, is recognized by its long, pinkish or reddish brown stem, 5—10cm × 1—2mm; the cap is parabolic to rounded conical, date-brown, drying paler, the dry region sharply demarcated.

Panaeolina (Panaeolus, Psilocybe) foenisecii Brown Hay Cap. Cap 1·5—2·5cm across, dull to reddish brown when moist, pale yellowish brown to cinnamon when dry, between very broadly rounded conical and strongly convex, not flattening. Gills pale brown and mottled, later umber, adnate; edge whitish. Stem 5—7·5cm × 2—4mm, brownish towards the base, paler above, smooth, fragile and hollow. Separated from *Panaeolus* by the somewhat brownish spores which are rough under the microscope. Occurs in short grass; February to December; common.

Chroogomphus (Gomphidius) rutilus (G. viscidus). Cap 3—15cm across, dull brown with a wine-coloured tinge, the margin yellowish, convex with a rather pronounced, sharp umbo, fleshy and slimy, paler and shining when dry. Gills dull olive, later purplish black, deeply decurrent, broad and widely spaced. Stem 6—12cm × 1—8mm, wine-coloured at the top, yellow-buff to ochre lower down, lemon-chrome at base, narrowing downwards, solid, with a slight, ring-like mark near the top at first. Flesh wine-coloured to salmon in cap, peach to apricot in stem and lemon-chrome at base, turning dark violet with iodine solutions. Occurs under pines; August to November; frequent. The genus *Gomphidius* differs in that the cap flesh is whitish and does not react with iodine. *G. roseus* is easily recognized by the coral cap and occurs under pines.

Coprinus
disseminatus

Panaeolus
sphinctrinus

Panaeolina
foenisecii

Chroogomphus
rutilus

Gasteromycetales Stomach fungi

Fungi belonging to this group are recognized by the spores being produced in masses either inside the fruit-body or at the top of a stalk that emerges from it. Key to genera:

1a   An evil-smelling slimy, spore mass is carried aloft at the top of a spongy
       stem   *Phallus, Mutinus* page 122
1b   The spore mass remains inside the fruit-body.
       2a   Spore mass hard at first, only powdery with age; fruit-body wall hard
              and thick   *Scleroderma* page 122
       2b   Spore mass soft, powdery at maturity; fruit-body wall soft and thin.
              3a   Outer wall of fruit-body splitting away in a star-like manner from
                     the inner   *Geastrum* page 122
              3b   Outer wall not separating from an inner one
                                                 Lycoperdon, Vascellum, Bovista see below

Lycoperdon Fruit-body globose to pear-shaped, with a hole at its top through which the powdery spores escape.

Lycoperdon perlatum Common Puff-ball *. Fruit-body 4—7cm high, 3—5cm across, white to greyish white, later yellowish and finally pale, dirty, yellowish brown, elongate pear-shaped or with a globose top on a wide, cylindrical, somewhat stem-like base; surface covered with short conical warts, each surrounded by a ring of smaller warts, leaving a net-like appearance when they fall off or are rubbed off. Flesh white at first, then yellow and finally forming a dusty, olive-brown spore mass, the outside wall remains as a thin, dry, papery envelope with a small hole at the top. Occurs in woods or on pastures; July to November; fairly common. *L. foetidum* (*perlatum* var. *nigrescens*) differs in that the warts are brown, thinner and more spine-like. It prefers more acid soils and coniferous woods. *L. echinatum* has even longer spines, up to 3—4mm long. *Calvatia* (*Lycoperdon*) *excipuliforme* (*L. saccatum*) *, resembles *L. perlatum* but is strongly pestle-shaped with a long, stem-like base and globose head. The surface warts are shortly spiny to granular and do not leave a net-like pattern when rubbed off. *Langermannia* (*Calvatia, Lycoperdon*) *giganteum* the Giant Puff-ball **, is globose, smooth, white; 15—30cm across. Finally dry and dull, dirty buff. They should not be eaten after the flesh turns yellowish.

Lycoperdon pyriforme Pear-shaped Puff-ball. Fruit-body 2·5 to 10cm high, 1—3cm wide, white or greyish, then pale brown, more or less pear-shaped, with an apical opening when mature; surface at first scurfy with tiny warts and granules; base has cord-like white strands. Flesh white, then greenish yellow, finally olive to brownish and dusty. Grows on decaying wood, often many together; August to November; common.

Vascellum (Lycoperdon) pratense (*L. hiemale, L. depressum*). Fruit-body 2—5cm across, globose, often flattened at the top, white, later yellowish, finally brown with a hole at the top; surface with small, white spines and granules which soon disappear. Flesh white, then yellowish, finally becoming a dark olive, dusty spore mass which is separated by a membrane from the spongy base. Occurs in short grass on lawns, etc.; August to November; common.

Bovista plumbea Fruit-body 3—6cm across, almost spherical and white at first; the outer layer then peels off and the inner layer becomes thin, papery and lead-coloured with a hole in the top. Flesh white, later olive and finally becoming a yellowish brown to olive-brown, dusty spore mass. Occurs on short grassland; throughout the year; common.

*Lycoperdon
perlatum*

*Lycoperdon
pyriforme*

*Vascellum
pratense*

Bovista plumbea

Geastrum (Geaster) triplex Earth Star. Fruit-body shaped like a tulip or an onion bulb when young, the outer layers later splitting away and rolling outwards and, often, under to form five to seven more or less pointed, fleshy lobes in a star-like arrangement. These are often cracked across their width and are flesh-coloured at first, then dark brown and more or less horny. In the centre of the star, which is 5–10cm across, is a globose, pale brown, stalkless sac, 1·5–3·5cm across with a small, conical mouth at the top, 14mm across. The sac contains a dusty, brown mass of spores. There is often a fleshy cup between the sac and the star-like lobes. Occurs on the ground in broad-leaved woods, often under beech, in parks or on sandy soils by the sea; September to October; occasional. *G. rufescens* is somewhat similar but smaller, 3–6cm across in mature specimens. The young fruit-body is globose, not pointed, the lobes are less fleshy and there is no cup between them and the central sac which is without a stalk.

Scleroderma citrinum (*S. aurantium, S. vulgare*) Common Earth-ball †. Fruit-body 4–8cm across, globose to pumpkin-shaped, sometimes shallowly lobed; surface firm, whitish or dull yellowish, cracking into small, flat, more or less brownish warts. The base is blunt and attached to mycelial cords. The flesh of the outer layer is 3–6mm thick, white and often becomes pinkish when cut. It surrounds an inner, hard mass, which is greyish, at first, then purplish black and with whitish veins, and finally dull brown and powdery. The fruit-body eventually splits open irregularly or decays away. Occurs on the ground in woods, on heaths, etc.; July to January; very common. Although reported as sometimes being used as a substitute for truffles, it is also said to have been the cause of serious poisoning. *S. verrucosum* is similar and occurs in the same places though less commonly, but is often larger, is thinner walled and is attached at the base by a mass of root-like cords. The spore mass is finally olive-brown.

Phallus impudicus Stinkhorn or Wood Witch. Fruit-body, when young, white or yellowish, egg-like to globose, 3–5cm across, with a thin skin covering a thick jelly layer which surrounds the compressed stem and spore mass. It is attached by a thick, white mycelial cord. At maturity the stem expands and breaks out of the egg and is topped by a thimble-like cap. Stem 10–30cm × 1–3cm, white, cylindrical, narrowing at both ends, spongy (like expanded polystyrene) and hollow. Cap 3–5cm high, attached only to the apex of the stem, covered with a slimy, blackish olive, foetid spore mass. This is removed eventually by flies feeding on it to reveal the white, honeycomb-like surface of the cap which has at its apex a small, white disc with a central hole. The foetid odour may be detected when several metres away. Occurs on the ground in woods and in gardens; May to November; common.

Mutinus caninus Dog Stinkhorn. The basic structure is similar to that of the last species. Young fruit-body 1–2cm across, pear-shaped or oval, white or yellowish, attached by a thick mycelial cord. Stem 6–9cm × 1cm, whitish or pinkish buff, spongy, tapering at the top and hollow. It has an orange-red head (not a separate cap), 2cm long, pointed and at first covered with a dark green, slimy spore mass with a faintly faecal odour. Occurs on the ground in woods and on old stumps; June to December; fairly common.

Geastrum triplex

Scleroderma citrinum

Phallus impudicus

Mutinus caninus

Glossary

adnate a gill attached to the stem by the greater part of its width, see fig. 5.

adnexed a gill attached to the stem by less than half its width, see fig. 5.

alkalis, caustic solutions of potassium or sodium hydroxide, usually employed at concentrations of around 20 per cent.

ammonia solution used either concentrated or diluted with an equal volume of water; household preparations may be adequate.

amyloid turning dull dark violet with iodine solutions. Tincture of iodine or watery solutions containing iodine and potassium iodide may be used. Melzer's reagent is best: dissolve 1gm of potassium iodide in 2cc of water and add 0·5gm of iodine; when dissolved add 18cc of water and finally 20gm of chloral hydrate. A spore deposit on glass (not on paper) may be tested by placing a drop of iodine solution on the margin and then tilting so that it runs off when any colour change of the deposit is easily seen.

anastomosing gills, ridges, veins, etc., which are joined together by cross-connections.

ascus (plural asci) see page 7.

basidium (plural basidia) see page 8.

bell-shaped a cap, strongly convex at the top but which becomes more or less concave lower down. See fig. 5.

cap a horizontal, flat or curved portion of a fruit-body, either supported by a central to lateral stem, or attached to one side, and carrying the spore-bearing surface. See page 9.

caustic alkalis see 'alkalis'.

conidium (plural conidia) a special type of spore produced in addition to the normal type formed in an ascus or on a basidium. See page 8.

convex a curved surface which is part of a sphere, but less than half. See fig. 5.

cortina see page 11.

cystidium (plural cystidia) distinctively shaped cells that sometimes occur between the basidia on a spore-bearing surface, or on the gill margin.

decurrent gills or tubes that run down the stem, see fig. 5.

emarginate a gill that appears as though a small portion has been removed where it joins the stem. See fig. 5.

fibrils small, fine threads or fibres found on the cap or stem surfaces.

fibrillose a surface covered with fibrils.

gill see page 9.

hygrophanous appearing water-soaked and darker coloured when moist, opaque and paler when dry.

hypha (plural hyphae) see page 6.

iodine solutions see 'amyloid'.

iron alum a largish crystal is rubbed on the surface to be tested. An iron sulphate crystal may be used instead.

membranous formed of a sheet of tissue that is thin, like a piece of paper.

mycelial cord or strand part of a mycelium in which a number of hyphae are united to form a thread or cord thick enough to be seen with the naked eye, and often attached to the base of a fruit-body.

mycelium see page 6.

ochre a dullish yellow at the orange end of the range of this colour.

olive a dull, dark, greenish brown or brownish green.

parabolic rounded conical with the margin convex. See fig. 5.

perithecium (plural perithecia). See page 7.

resupinate a fruit-body whose underneath surface is more or less completely attached to the surface on which it is growing and covers it like a crust.

ring see page 10.

sepia a dull, dark, neutral brown i.e. one that is neither reddish nor yellowish.

scurfy a surface covered with small, flattish, scurf-like particles.

sinuate a gill attached to the stem by a small, more or less extended 's'-shaped portion. See fig. 5.

spore see page 6.

striate marked with a series of parallel lines or veins.

subglobose nearly but not quite globular in shape.

tawny orangy brown or brownish orange.

tubercle a small, more or less rounded but irregular outgrowth.

tubercular covered with tubercles.

umber a dark, somewhat reddish brown.

umbilicate a cap with a small, central, often funnel-shaped depression like a navel. See fig. 5.

umbo a raised area in the centre of a cap that may be flat, rounded or conical.

umbonate having an umbo. See fig. 5.

veil see page 10.

volva see page 10.

Fig. 5 Longitudinal sections of caps to show terms used for their shape and gill attachment.

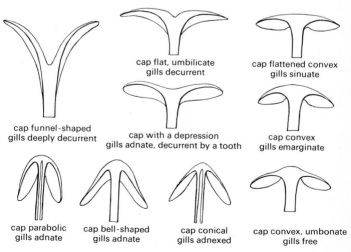

cap funnel-shaped
gills deeply decurrent

cap flat, umbilicate
gills decurrent

cap with a depression
gills adnate, decurrent by a tooth

cap flattened convex
gills sinuate

cap convex
gills emarginate

cap parabolic
gills adnate

cap bell-shaped
gills adnate

cap conical
gills adnexed

cap convex, umbonate
gills free

Index

126

Acknowledgements

Photographs
Agenteur Photo-Center — Raab 45 UC; Heather Angel, Farnham, title page, 15T, 21B, 27UC, 35T, 39LC, 61T, 65T, 71LC, 77UC, 93UC, 97B, 99T, 101T, 123T, back cover; Aquila — A. J. Bond 73B; Aquila — Hartley Travis 39UC, 69UC, 97LC, 101LC; Bavaria Verlag — Christian Lederer 51T; Biofotos — Gordon Dickson 17LC, 27B, 65UC, 81T, 89LC, 91UC, 105B, 107UC, 121LC; Edward Blackwell, Wolverhampton 27T, 41T, 47T, 53UC, 61LC, 75T, 77T, 83T, 83LC, 89UC, 95B, 99B, 109UC, 111B, 115UC; A. W. Brand, Stratford-on-Avon 19T, 19UC, 31LC, 33B, 35LC, 35B, 37T, 37B, 39T, 41UC, 41B, 43B, 45LC, 45B, 47UC, 49UC, 49B, 55LC, 57T, 59UC, 59B, 63UC, 65LC, 65B, 67B, 69B, 71B, 79UC, i5LC, 95UC, 103T, 105UC, 109B, 113B, 117B, 119T, 119LC, 121UC, 123B; V. L. Breeze, Lewes 21UC, 49T, 49UC, 101UC, 103LC; British Mycological Society 119B; British Mycological Society — S. C. Porter 37UC, 79T, 95T, 107B; Hervé Chaumeton, Chamalières 17UC, 17B, 19LC, 21LC, 29UC, 47B, 51UC, 53B, 55B, 57UC, 59T, 61UC, 73LC, 77LC, 77B, 81UC, 89T, 109T, 111LC, 115LC, 121T; Bruce Coleman — S. C. Porter 61B, 115T; W. F. Davidson, Penrith 19B, 21T, 81B, 87T, 119UC; Breck Kent — Dr E. R. Degginger 85T; D. M. Dring 121B; Mavis Hards, Littlehampton 23LC; David Hosking, London 113T; Jacana — Hervé Chaumeton 73T, 117LC; Jacana — R. König 113LC; Jacana — Claude Nardin 43UC, 67LC, 101B, 105LC; Jacana — Pierre Pilloud 47LC; Jacana — Marie Cécile Robert 69T; Frank Lane — Heinz Schrempp 29LC, 31T, 31B, 35UC, 41LC, 43LC, 53T, 57B, 67UC, 89B, 95LC; Frank Lane — Harry Wright 117T, 123LC; Mike Leach, Telford 23UC; R. W. Rayner, Middleton-on-Sea 15LC, 17T, 23B, 33LC, 37LC, 55T, 71T, 81LC, 87UC, 99UC, 107LC, 111UC, 123UC; Natural History Photographic Agency — Stephen Dalton 63LC; Natural History Photographic Agency — Brian Hawkes 83B, 97T, 107T, 113UC, 117UC; Natural History Photographic Agency — K. G. Preston-Mafham 15UC, 15B, 23T, 25T, 25LC, 29T, 33T, 51B, 55UC, 57LC, 63T, 63B, 79B, 85UC, 87B, 91LC, 93LC, 97UC, 105T, 109LC; Alan Outen, Flitwick 33UC, 53LC, 59LC, 75LC, 75B, 79LC, 85B, 93T, 103UC; D. A. Reid, Kew 25UC, 27LC, 31UC, 69LC, 83UC, 103B, 111T; P. Stiles, London 29B, 43T, 71UC, 73UC, 87LC, 91B, 93T; D. Ward, Virginia Water 51LC, 91T, 99LC; Professor John Webster, Exeter 25B; N. A. J. Wilde, Wolverhampton 39B, 67T, 75UC, 115B; ZEFA — Podschies 45T. Peter Loughran, front jacket.

(T — top, UC — upper centre, LC — lower centre, B — bottom)

128